Radio Operator's License Q & A Manual Supplement No. 3

MILTON KAUFMAN

LIBRARY OF CONGRESS CATALOG CARD NUMBER 57-11293

Printed in the United States of America

PREFACE TO SUPPLEMENT NO. 3

In January 1965, a new FCC Study Guide Supplement was issued. This supplement is the basis of revised examinations beginning in February 1966. The Elements which have undergone the greatest revision are Elements III and IV. The FCC Supplement also contains Elements I, II and IX. However, except for some very minor revisions to Element IX, these are unchanged. In addition, Elements V, VI, VII and VIII remain unchanged. In the Preface to the main book, the student will find listed, the requirements for all the classes of licenses and endorsements.

Applicants for a Second Class Radiotelephone Operator's License will find all the required Questions and Answers (including references to the main book) for Elements I, II and III, in this Supplement No. 3.

Applicants for a First Class Radiotelephone Operator's License will presently use Elements I, II and III in Supplement No. 3, and Element IV as it appears in the main book. At a later date, the FCC will examine Element IV on the basis of the new questions in their January 1965 Study Guide Supplement. At that time new material will be issued containing the complete questions and answers for the revised Element IV. Students are advised, during this changeover period, to consult the FCC with regard to whether the old or new Element IV is in force, before attempting to study this Element.

Applicants for a Third Class Radiotelephone Operator's License will use Elements I and II in this Supplement No. 3.

Two types of Element II examination are now available. One is of a general nature; the other is for candidates specializing in ship and coastal radiotelephony. Element II consists of 20 questions. These are of the multiple-choice type and carry a credit of 5 percent each. An applicant not desiring the new Broadcast Endorsement is required only to pass Elements I and II. (75 percent is passing grade for all examinations.) However, if a Broadcast Endorsement is desired, Elements I, II and IX must be passed. With a Broadcast Endorsement, an operator may routinely operate the following stations:

1. AM stations with a power of 10 kw or less and utilizing a non-directional antenna.

2. FM stations with a transmitter power output of 25 kw or less. Provided that a supervisory operator holding a Radiotelephone First Class Operator License is employed either on a full- or part-time basis. At cer-

tain non-commercial, educational stations, the supervisory operator may be the holder of a Second Class Operator License.

Applicants for all classes of radiotelegraph licenses will use Elements I, and II in this Supplement No. 3 and the balance of the required Elements in the main book.

To achieve proper utilization of this Supplement and of the main body of the book, it is vital that the reader carefully study the instructions in "How to Use This Supplement," which follows.

The author is deeply grateful to Mr. Ed Williamson of RCA Institutes for his invaluable assistance with some portions of Element III. Many thanks are due to Mr. Bernard Grob of RCA Institutes for his assistance during the preparation of the manuscript. In addition, the author wishes to express his appreciation to his wife, Hazel, for typing the manuscript.

Milton Kaufman

New Hyde Park, N.Y.
February, 1966

HOW TO USE THIS SUPPLEMENT

In this Supplement No. 3, all questions are presented in the exact order and wording as they appear in the FCC (Jan. 1965) Supplement.

ELEMENTS I AND II

Elements I and II are presented in their entirety in this Supplement. The reader may disregard all other information on these Elements appearing in the main body of the book.

ELEMENT III

The questions in Element III have in many cases, been revised. The total number of questions has been reduced, but some questions now consist of a number of parts. The questions in Element III have been categorized according to general topics as follows:

1. Alternating and direct current.
2. Electron tubes.
3. Indicating instruments.
4. Oscillators.
5. Audio amplifiers.
6. Radio frequency amplifiers.
7. Transmitters.
8. Amplitude modulation.
9. Frequency modulation.
10. Transistors.
11. Antennas.
12. Transmission lines.
13. Frequency measurements.
14. Batteries.
15. Motors and generators.
16. Microwave equipment.

The answers to each question in Element III may appear in any of the following forms:

1. As references to one or more questions and answers in the main book.

2. As completely new answers to questions.

3. As references to the main book plus some additional new material; as may be required.

Unless otherwise noted, all references to other questions refer to the main book.

ELEMENT IV

The revised Element IV, of necessity, does not presently appear in this Supplement No. 3. Refer to the Preface of Supplement No. 3 for further explanation.

ELEMENTS V, VI, VII, VIII

Elements V, VI, VII, and VIII are unchanged and appear only in the main book.

ELEMENT IX

Element IX as it appears in Supplement No. 2 (in all *Q & A Manuals* published since 1964) is timely and accurate and may be used, except for the following information:

1. Q. 9.31 has been added.

Question 9.31. If the tower lights of a station are required to be controlled by a light-sensitive device, and this device malfunctions, when should the tower lights be "on"? (R & R 17.25(a) (3))

Answer. All lights shall burn continuously or shall be controlled by a light sensitive device adjusted so that the lights will be turned on at a north sky light intensity level of about 35 foot candles and turned off at a north sky light intensity level of about 58 foot candles.

2. The R & R reference part numbers of the FCC publications have in some cases been changed. In every case of Element IX, where Part 3 is indicated (i.e. R & R 3.115), change to Part 73 (i.e. R & R 73.115). In addition, add these R & R references to questions as indicated:

a. Q. 9.06 (R & R 73.14)
b. Q. 9.07 (R & R 73.59)
c. Q. 9.08 (R & R 73.93b, 73.265b)
d. Q. 9.11 (R & R 73.111)

ELEMENT I

BASIC LAW

(Note: References which appear after questions in all Elements give the law or regulation involved in answering the questions. Abbreviations used are as follows: Sec. refers to a section of the Communications Act of 1934; Art. refers to an article of the International Radio Regulations (Atlantic City, 1947); R & R refers to provision of the Rules and Regulations of the Federal Communications Commission; and GLR refers to regulations annexed to the Agreement Between the United States and Canada for Promotion of Safety and the Great Lakes by Means of Radio.)

Question 1.01. Where and how are FCC licenses and permits obtained? (R & R 13.11(a))

Answer.   In general, an operator liense or permit is obtained by making application to the regional FCC office and by passing such examination elements as are required for the particular class of license desired. In the case of a restricted radiotelephone permit, no written or oral examination is required, but proper application must be made.

Discussion.   See "Preface" of the main book for a list of requirements regarding the various classes of licenses and endorsements.

Q. 1.02.   When a licensee qualifies for a higher grade of FCC license or permit, what happens to the lesser grade license? (R & R 13.26)

A.   If the higher grade of license is in the same group, the lesser grade will be cancelled upon the issuance of a new license.

Q. 1.03.   Who may apply for an FCC license? (R & R 13.5(a))

A.   Normally, commercial licenses are issued only to citizens and other nationals of the United States of America.

D.   As an exception, in the case of an alien who holds an Aircraft Pilot certificate issued by the FAA and is lawfully in the United States, the Commission may waive the requirements of U.S. nationality.

Q. 1.04.   If a license or permit is lost, what action must be taken by the operator? (R & R 13.71, 13.72)

A.   An operator whose license or permit has been lost, mutilated or destroyed shall immediately notify the Commission.

D. An application for a duplicate should be submitted to the office of issue embodying a statement attesting to the facts thereof. If a license has been lost, the applicant must state that reasonable search has been made for it, and further, that in the event it be found either the original or the duplicate will be returned for cancellation. The applicant must also give a statement of the service that has been obtained under the lost license.

Q. 1.05. What is the usual license term for radio operators? (R & R 13.4(a))

A. Five (5) years.

Q. 1.06. What government agency inspects radio stations in the U.S.? (Sec. 303(n))

A. The Federal Communications Commission.

D. The licensee of any radio station shall make the station available for inspection by representatives of the Commission at any reasonable hour and under the regulations governing the class of station concerned.

Q. 1.07. When may a license be renewed? (R & R 13.11)

A. Within one year before expiration.

D. However, a grace period exists which extends the renewal time to one year after the expiration of the license. Of course, the licensee may *not* operate with an expired license.

Q. 1.08. Who keeps the station logs? (R & R 73.111)

A. The licensee or permittee of each broadcast station.

D. Each log shall be kept by the person or persons competent to do so, having actual knowledge of the facts required. Such person(s) shall sign the appropriate log when starting duty and again when going off duty.

Q. 1.09. Who corrects errors in the station logs? (R & R 73.111)

A. Any necessary correction may be made only by the person originating the entry who shall strike out the erroneous portion, initial the correction made, and indicate the date of correction.

Q. 1.10. How may errors in the station logs be corrected? (R & R 73.111)

A. See Question 1.09, above.

Q. 1.11. Under what conditions may messages be rebroadcast? (Sec. 325(a))

A.   No broadcasting station shall rebroadcast the program or any part thereof of another broadcasting station without the express authority of the originating station.

Q. 1.12. What messages and signals may not be transmitted? (R & R 13.66, 13.67, 13.68)

A.   The following may not be transmitted:

1. Unnecessary, unidentified, or superfluous radio communications or signals.

2. Obscene, indecent, or profane language or meaning.

3. False or deceptive signals or communications by radio, or any call letter or signal which has not been assigned by proper authority to the radio station being operated.

Q. 1.13. May an operator deliberately interfere with any radio communication or signal? (R & R 13.69)

A.   No.

D.   No operator shall willfully or maliciously interfere with or cause interference to any radio communication or signal.

Q. 1.14. What type of communication has top priority in the mobile service? (Art. 37)

A.   Top priority is given to distress calls, distress messages, and distress traffic.

D.   The order of priority for other communications is as follows:

1. Communications preceded by the urgency signal.

2. Communications preceded by the safety signal.

3. Communications relating to radio-direction finding.

4. Communications relating to the navigation and safe movement of aircraft.

5. Communications relating to the navigation, movements, and needs of ships and weather observation messages destined for an official, meteorological service.

6. Government radio telegrams: Priorité Nations.

7. Government communications for which priority has been requested.

8. Service communications relating to the working of the radio communications previously exchanged.

9. Government communications other than those shown in 6 and 7 above and all other communications.

Q. 1.15. What are the grounds for suspension of operator licenses? (Sec. 303(m) (1))

A.   The FCC has authority to suspend the license of any operator upon proof sufficient to satisfy the Commission that the licensee—

1. Has violated any provision of any act, treaty, or convention binding on the United States, which the Commission is authorized to administer, or any regulation made by the Commission under any such act, treaty, or convention; or

2. Has failed to carry out a lawful order of the master or person lawfully in charge of the ship or aircraft on which he is employed; or

3. Has willfully damaged or permitted radio apparatus or installations to be damaged; or

4. Has transmitted superfluous radio communications or signals or communications containing profane or obscene words, language, or meaning, or has knowingly transmitted false or deceptive signals or communications, or a call signal or letter which has not been assigned by proper authority to the station he is operating; or

5. Has willfully or maliciously interfered with any other radio communications or signals; or

6. Has obtained or attempted to obtain, or has assisted another to obtain or attempt to obtain, an operator's license by fraudulent means.

Q. 1.16. When may an operator divulge the contents of an intercepted message? (Sec. 605)

A.   Only in the case of a radio communication broadcast transmitted by amateurs or others for the use of the general public; or in the case of messages relating to ships (or aircraft) in distress.

Q. 1.17. If a licensee is notified that he has violated an FCC rule or provision of the Communication Act of 1934, what must he do? (R & R 1.89)

A.   Within 10 days from receipt of notice or such other period as may be specified, the licensee shall send a written answer, in duplicate, direct to the office of the Commission originating the official notice. If an answer cannot be sent nor an acknowledgment made within such 10-day period by reason of illness or other unavoidable circumstances, acknowledgment and answer shall be made at the earliest practicable date with a satisfactory explanation of the delay.

D.   The answer to each notice shall be complete in itself and shall not be abbreviated by reference to other communications or answers to other notices. In every instance the answer shall contain a statement of action taken to correct the condition or omission complained of and to preclude its recurrence. In addition: If the notice relates to violations that may be due to the physical or electrical characteristics of transmitting apparatus and any new apparatus is to be installed, the answer shall state the date such apparatus was ordered, the name of the manufacturer, and the promised date of delivery. If the installation of such apparatus requires a construction permit, the file number of the application shall be given, or if a file number has not been assigned by the Commission, such identification shall be given as will permit ready identification of the application. If the notice of violation relates to lack of attention to or improper operation of the transmitter, the name and license number of the operator in charge shall be given.

Q. 1.18. If a licensee receives a notice of suspension of his license, what must he do? (R & R 1.85)

A. He shall make written application for a hearing to the Commission (FCC) within 15 days of receipt of notice.

D. Whenever grounds exist for suspension of an operator license, as provided in section 303(m) of the Communications Act, the Chief of the Safety and Special Radio Services Bureau, with respect to amateur operator licenses, or the Chief of the Field Engineering Bureau, with respect to commercial operator licenses, may issue an order suspending the operator license. No order of suspension of any operator's license shall take effect until 15 days' notice in writing of the cause for the proposed suspension has been given to the operator licensee, who may make written application to the Commission at any time within said 15 days for a hearing upon such order. The notice to the operator licensee shall not be effective until actually received by him, and from that time he shall have 15 days in which to mail the said application. In the event that physical conditions prevent mailing of the application before the expiration of the 15-day period, the application shall then be mailed as soon as possible thereafter, accompanied by a satisfactory explanation of the dealy.

Q. 1.19. What are the penalties provided for violating a provision of the Communications Act of 1934 or a Rule of the FCC? (Sec. 501, 502)

A. (a) Any person who willfully and knowingly does or causes or suffers to be done any act, matter, or thing, in the Communications Act, prohibited or declared to be unlawful, or who willfully and knowingly omits or fails to do any act, matter, or thing in this Act required to be done, or upon conviction thereof, shall be punished by such offense, for which no penalty (other than forfeiture) is provided therein, by a fine of not more than $10,000 or by imprisonment for a term of not more than two years, or both.

(b) For violation of a Rule of the FCC, a fine of not more than $500 per day for each and every day of the offense is stipulated.

Q. 1.20. Define "harmful interference." (Section III, Geneva, 1959, Treaty)

A. "Harmful interference" encompasses the following: any emission, radiation, or induction which endangers the functioning of a radionavigation service or of other safety services, or which seriously degrades, obstructs, or repeatedly interrupts a radiocommunication service operating in accordance with these Regulations.

ELEMENT II

BASIC OPERATING PRACTICE

(Note: The questions of Element II have been subdivided into two categories. The candidate for a license may elect to answer questions in the general category (O), or to answer questions in marine category (M)).

CATEGORY "O" — GENERAL

Q. 2.01. What should an operator do when he leaves a transmitter unattended?

A. If an operator leaves a transmitter unattended, the transmitter must be made inaccessible or inoperable with respect to all unauthorized persons.

Q. 2.02. What are the meanings of clear, out, over, roger, words twice, say again, and break?

A. 1. The word "clear" signifies that the transmission is ended and that no response is expected.

2. The word "out" signifies that the conversation is ended and that no response is expected.

3. The word "over" signifies "My transmission is ended and I expect a response from you."

4. The word "roger" signifies "I have received all of your last transmission."

5. The words "words twice" means:

    (a) As a request: "Communication is difficult. Please send every phrase twice."

    (b) As information: "Since communication is difficult every phrase in this message will be sent twice."

6. The words "say again" signifies repeat.

7. The word "break" signifies a separation between portions of a message.

Q. 2.03. How should a microphone be treated when used in noisy locations?

A. The microphone should be shielded with the hands in order to reduce outside noises thus making communications wave intelligible.

D. In severe cases, special noise-cancelling microphones may be used.

Q. 2.04. What may happen to the received signal when an operator has shouted into a microphone?

A. Shouting into the microphone is poor practice, because while it probably will not injure the microphone, it may very well overdrive some speech amplifier or cause overmodulation. Either of these effects may cause severe distortion of the speech and possible interference with adjacent channels.

Q. 2.05. Why should radio transmitters be "off" when signals are not being transmitted?

A. To prevent interference with other stations using the channel.

D. Even if an unmodulated carrier is transmitted, it may cause heterodyning interference with other station carriers, making communication very difficult.

Q. 2.06. Why should an operator use well-known words and phrases?

A. The operator should use simple language and well-known words and phrases to insure accurate, efficient communications and to eliminate repetition as much as possible.

Q. 2.07. Why is the station's call sign transmitted?

A. The station's call sign should be transmitted in order to clearly identify the originator of messages being transmitted.

Q. 2.08. Where does an operator find specifications for obstruction marking and lighting (where required) for the antenna towers of a particular radio station?

A. Specifications are found in Part 17 of the Rules and Regulations of the FCC. (R & R 17.37 and 17.38.)

Q. 2.09. What should an operator do if he hears profanity being used at his station?

A. He should take steps to conclude the transmission and enter the details in the station log. The incident should be reported to the FCC.

Q. 2.10. When may an operator use his station without regard to certain provisions of his station license? (R & R 2.405)

A. The licensee of any station, except amateur, may, during a period of emergency in which normal communication facilities are disrupted as a result of hurricane, flood, earthquake or similar disaster, utilize such station for emergency communication service in communicating in a manner other than that specified in the instrument of authorization.

Q. 2.11. Who bears the responsibility if an operator permits an unlicensed person to speak over his station?

A. The licensed operator in charge of the station always bears the responsibility for its operation, regardless of who is speaking over it.

Q. 2.12. What is meant by a "phonetic alphabet" in radiotelephone communications?

A. A phonetic alphabet is one in which each letter is associated with a particular word. For example: A—Able, B—Baker, C—Charlie, D—Dog, etc.

D. A phonetic alphabet is used in radiotelephone communication to insure that certain letters or words are clearly understandable to the receiving station.

Q. 2.13. How does the licensed operator of a station normally exhibit his authority to operate the station?

A. The original license of each station operator shall be posted at the place where he is on duty or kept in his possession in the manner specified in the regulations governing the class of station concerned.

Q. 2.14. What precautions should be observed in testing a station on the air?

A. The operator should listen on the transmission frequency to insure that interference will not be caused to a communication in progress.

CATEGORY "M" — MARINE

Q. 2.01. What is the importance of the frequency 2182 kc? (R & R 83.352, 83.353(a))

A. This frequency may be used in two ways:
1. It is the international distress frequency for radiotelephony, ships, aircraft and survival-craft stations.
2. It is the international general radiotelephone calling frequency for the maritime mobile service.

Q. 2.02. Describe completely what actions should be taken by a radio operator who hears a distress message; a safety message. (R & R 83.239, 83.240, 83.241, 83.242)

A. 1. How to acknowledge a distress message:

(a) Stations of the maritime mobile service which receive a distress message from a mobile station which is, beyond any possible doubt, in their vicinity, shall immediately acknowledge receipt. However, in areas where reliable communication with one or more coast stations are practicable, ship stations may defer this acknowledgment for a short interval so that a coast station may acknowledge receipt.

(b) Stations of the maritime mobile service which receive a distress message from a mobile station which, beyond any possible doubt, is not in their vicinity, shall allow a short interval of time to elapse before acknowledging receipt of the message, in order to permit stations nearer to the mobile station in distress to acknowledge receipt without interference.

2. Form of acknowledgment:

(a) The acknowledgment of receipt of a distress message is transmitted, when radiotelegraphy is used, in the following form:

(1) The call sign of the station sending the distress message, sent three times;

(2) The word DE;

(3) The call sign of the station acknowledging receipt, sent three times;

(4) The group RRR;

(5) The distress signal SOS.

(b) The acknowledgment of receipt of a distress message is transmitted, when radiotelephony is used, in the following form:

(1) The call sign or other identification of the station sending the distress message, spoken three times;

(2) The words THIS IS;

(3) The call sign or other identification of the station acknowledging receipt, spoken three times;

(4) The word RECEIVED;

(5) The distress signal MAYDAY.

3. Information furnished by acknowledging station:

(a) Every mobile station which acknowledges receipt of a distress message shall, on the order of the master or person responsible for the ship, aircraft, or other vehicle carrying such mobile station, transmit as soon as possible the following information in the order shown:

(1) Its name;

(2) Its position, in the form prescribed in R & R 83.236(c);

(3) The speed at which it is proceeding towards, and the approximate time it will take to reach, the mobile station in distress.

(b) Before sending this message, the station shall ensure that it will not interfere with the emissions of other stations better situated to render immediate assistance to the station in distress.

4. Transmission of distress message by a station not itself in distress:

(a) A mobile station or a land station which learns that a mobile station is in distress shall transmit a distress message in any of the following cases:

(1) When the station in distress is not itself in a position to transmit the distress message;

(2) When the master or person responsible for the ship, aircraft, or other vehicle not in distress, or the person responsible for the land station, considers that further help is necessary;

(3) When, although not in a position to render assistance, it has heard a distress message which has not been acknowledged. When a mobile station transmits a distress message under these conditions, it shall take all necessary steps to notify the authorities who may be able to render assistance.

(b) The transmission of a distress message under the conditions prescribed in paragraph (a) of this section shall be made on either or both of the international distress frequencies (500 kc/s radiotelegraph; 2182 kc/s radiotelephone) or on any other available frequency on which attention might be attracted.

(c) The transmission of the distress message shall always be preceded by the call indicated below, which shall itself be preceded whenever possible by the radiotelegraph or radiotelephone alarm signal. This call consists of:

(1) When radiotelegraphy is used:

(i) The signal DDD SOS SOS SOS DDD;

(ii) The word DE.

(iii) The call sign of the transmitting station, sent three times;

(2) When radiotelephony is used:

(i) The signal MAYDAY RELAY, spoken three times;

(ii) The words THIS IS;

(iii) The call sign or other identification of the transmitting station, spoken three times.

(d) When the radiotelegraph alarm signal is used, an interval of two minutes shall be allowed, whenever this is considered necessary, before the transmission of the call mentioned.

5. Safety Message: A safety message is one which provides information concerning the safety of navigation, or important meteorological warnings. A radio operator receiving such a message should immediately forward the message to the ship's master.

Q. 2.03. What information must be contained in distress messages? What procedure should be followed by a radio operator in sending a distress message? What is a good choice of words to be used in sending a distress message? (R & R 83.234 through 83.238)

A. 1. The following information must be contained in distress messages:

The message shall include the distress call followed by the name of the ship, aircraft, or the vehicle in distress, information regarding the position of the latter, the nature of the distress and the nature of the help requested, and any other further information which might facilitate this assistance.

2. The following procedure should be followed:

(a) Distress signals:

(1) The international radiotelegraph distress signal consists of the group "three dots, three dashes, three dots" (...————...), symbolized herein by SOS, transmitted as a single signal in which the dashes are slightly prolonged so as to be distinguished clearly from the dots.

(2) The international radiotelephone distress signal consists of the word MAYDAY, pronounced as the French expression "m'aider."

(3) These distress signals indicate that a mobile station is threatened by grave and imminent danger and requests immediate assistance.

(b) Radiotelephone distress call and message transmission procedure:

(1) The radiotelephone distress procedure shall consist of:

(i) The radiotelephone alarm signal (whenever possible);

(ii) The distress call;

(iii) The distress message.

(2) The radiotelephone distress transmissions shall be made slowly and distinctly, each word being clearly pronounced to facilitate transcription.

(3) After the transmission by radiotelephony of its distress message, the mobile station may be requested to transmit suitable signals followed by its call sign or name, to permit direction-finding stations to determine its position. This request may be repeated at frequent intervals if necessary.

(4) The distress message, preceded by the distress call, shall be repeated at intervals until an answer is received. This repetition shall be preceded by the radiotelephone alarm signal whenever possible.

(5) When the mobile station in distress receives no answer to a distress message transmitted on the distress frequency, the message may be repeated on any other available frequency on which attention might be attracted.

3. A suitable choice of words would be "Mayday, Mayday, Mayday, this is Trans Ocean Airlines Flight 907, 14 miles due East of Cape Hatteras, three engines out, require immediate assistance to pick up all on board after ditching. Estimate ditching to occur in 30 seconds; number 3 engine on fire, Over."

Q. 2.04. **What are the requirements for keeping watch on 2182 Kc? If a radio operator is required to "stand watch" on an international distress frequency, when may he stop listening? (R & R 83.223)**

A. 1. The requirements are as follows:

(a) Each ship station on board a ship navigating the Great Lakes and licensed to transmit by telephony on one or more frequencies within the band 1600 to 3500 kc/s shall, during its hours of service for telephony, maintain an efficient watch for the reception of class A3 emission on the radio-channel of which 2182 kc/s is the assigned frequency, whenever the station is not being used for transmission on that channel or for communication on other radio-channels.

(b) Except for stations on board vessels required by law to be fitted with radiotelegraph equipment, each ship station (in addition to those ship stations specified in paragraph (a) of this section) licensed to transmit by telephony on one or more frequencies within the band 1600 to 3500 kc/s shall, during its hours of service for telephony, maintain an efficient watch for the reception of class A3 emission on the radio-channel of which 2182 kc/s is the assigned frequency, whenever such station is not being used for transmission on that channel or for communication on other radio-channels. When the ship station is in Region 1 or 3, such watch shall, insofar as is possible, be maintained at least twice each hour for three minutes commencing at x h. 00 and x h. 30, Greenwich Mean Time (G. M. T.).

2. He may stop listening whenever the station is being used for transmission on that channel or for communication on other radio-channels.

Q. 2.05.   Under what circumstances may a coast station contact a land station by radio? (R & R 81.302(a) (2))

A. For the purpose of facilitating the transmission or reception of safety communication to or from a ship or aircraft station.

Q. 2.06.   What do distress, safety, and urgency signals indicate? What are the international urgency, safety, and distress signals? In the case of a mobile radio station in distress what station is responsible for the control of distress message traffic? (R & R 83.234 through 83.249)

A. 1. (a) The distress signal (MAYDAY) indicates that the ship, aircraft or any other vehicle which sends the distress signal is threatened by serious and imminent danger and requests immediate assistance.

(b) The safety signal (SECURITY) announces that the station is about to transmit a message concerning the safety of navigation or giving important meteorological warnings. Hence, it should precede such a transmission.

(c) The urgent signal (PAN) shall indicate that the calling station has a very urgent message to transmit concerning the safety of a ship, an aircraft, or another vehicle, or concerning the safety of some person on board or sighted from on board.

2. The control of distress traffic shall be the responsibility of the mobile station in distress or upon the station which, by application of the provisions of the Commission's rules and regulations has sent the

distress call. These stations may delegate the control of the distress traffic to another station.

Q. 2.07. In regions of heavy traffic why should an interval be left between radiotelephone calls? Why should a radio operator listen before transmitting on a shared channel? How long may a radio operator in the mobile service continue attempting to contact a station which does not answer? (R & R 83.366)

A. 1. An interval should be left (and is required by law) to permit other stations to share the radio channel. (See R & R 83.366 for details.)

2. He should listen on the shared channel first to avoid disrupting communication which may already be in progress.

3. Calling a particular station shall not continue for more than 30 seconds in each instance. If the called station is not heard to reply, that station shall not again be called until after an interval of 2 minutes. When a station called does not reply to a call sent three times at intervals of 2 minutes, the calling shall cease and shall not be renewed until after an interval of 15 minutes; however, if there is no reason to believe that harmful interference will be caused to other communications in progress, the call sent three times at intervals of 2 minutes may be repeated after a pause of not less than 3 minutes. In event of an emergency involving safety, the provisions of this paragraph shall not apply.

Q. 2.08. Why are test transmissions sent? How often should they be sent? What is the proper way to send a test message? How often should the station's call sign be sent? (R & R 83.365)

A. 1. Test transmissions are sent to insure that the radio equipment is functioning normally.

2. They should be sent each day unless normal use of the radiotelephone installation demonstrates that the equipment is in proper operating condition.

3. The official call sign of the testing station, followed by the word "test," shall be announced on the radio-channel being used for the test, as a warning that test emissions are about to be made on that frequency.

4. The station's call sign shall be sent at the conclusion of each test message, which should not exceed 10 seconds.

D. If, as a result of the announcement prescribed in subparagraph 3. above, any station transmits by voice the word "wait," testing shall be suspended. When, after an appropriate interval of time, such announcement is repeated and no response is observed, and careful listening indicates that harmful interference should not be caused the operator shall proceed as follows:

The operator shall announce the word "testing" followed in the case of a voice transmission test by the count "1, 2, 3, 4 * * * etc." or by test phrases or sentences not in conflict with normal operating signals; or followed, in the case of other emission, by appropriate test signals not in conflict with normal operating signals. The test signals in either case shall have a duration not exceeding ten seconds. At the conclusion of the test, there shall be voice announcement of the official call sign of the testing station, the name of the ship on which the station is located, and the general location of the ship at the time the test is being made. This test transmission shall not be repeated until a period of at least one minute has elapsed; on the frequency 2182 kc/s or 156.8 mc/s in a region of heavy traffic, a period of at least five minutes shall elapse before the test transmission is repeated.

When testing is conducted on any frequency assignment within the band 2170 kc/s to 2194 kc/s, within the band 156.75 mc/s to 156.85 mc/s, within the band 480 kc/s to 510 kc/s (lifeboat transmitters only), or within the band 8362 kc/s to 8366 kc/s (lifeboat transmitters only), no test transmissions shall occur which are likely to actuate any automatic alarm receiver within range. Lifeboat stations using telephony shall not be tested on the assigned frequency 500 kc/s during the 500 kc/s silence periods.

If a radio station is used only for occasional calls, it is a good practice to test the station regularly. Regular tests may reveal defects or faults which, if corrected immediately may prevent delays when communications are necessary. Caution should be observed by persons testing a station to make certain their test message will not interfere with other communications in progress in the same channel. Technical repairs or adjustments to radio telephone communication stations are made only by or under the immediate supervision and responsibility of operators holding first or second-class licenses.

Q. 2.09. In the mobile service, why should radiotelephone messages be as brief as possible?

A. It is a good policy to be brief to permit other stations to operate without interference and also from the standpoint of efficient station operations.

Q. 2.10.   What are the meanings of: Clear, Out, Over, Roger, Words Twice, Repeat, and Break?

A.   See Q. 2.02, above (Category "O" — General).

Q. 2.11   Does the Geneva, 1959 treaty give other countries the authority to inspect U. S. vessels? (Art. 21)

A.   Yes.

D.   The governments or appropriate administrations of countries which a mobile station visits, may require the production of the license for examination. The operator of the mobile station, or the person responsible for the station, shall facilitate this examination. The license shall be kept in such a way that it can be produced upon request. As far as possible, the license, or a copy certified by the authority which has issued it, should be permanently exhibited in the station.

Q. 2.12. Why are call signs sent? Why should they be sent clearly and distinctly?

A. 1. Call signs are sent to enable monitoring stations to identify the station of origin.

2. They should be sent clearly and distinctly to avoid unneccessary repetition and to assist monitoring stations in identifying calls.

Q. 2.13. How does the licensed operator of a ship station exhibit his authority to operate a station? (R & R 83.156)

A. When a licensed operator is required for the operation of a station, the original license of each such operator while he is employed or designated as radio operator of the station shall be posted in a conspicuous place at the principal location on board ship at which the station is operated: Provided, that in the case of stations of a portable nature, including marine-utility stations, or in the case where the operator holds a restricted radiotelephone operator permit, the operator may in lieu of posting have on his person either his required operator license or a duly issued verification card (FCC form 758-F) attesting to the existence of that license.

Q. 2.14. When may a coast station NOT charge for messages it is requested to handle? (R & R 81.179)

A. 1. No charge shall be made by any station in the maritime mobile service of the United States for the transmission of distress messages and replies thereto in connection with situations involving the safety of life and property at sea.

2. No charge shall be made by any station in the maritime mobile service of the United States for the transmission receipt, or relay of the information concerning dangers to navigation, originating on a ship of the United States or of a foreign country.

Q. 2.15. What is the difference between calling and working frequencies? (R & R 83.6)

A. A calling frequency is one to which all stations generally listen, for example 500 kilocycles. A working frequency is an assigned frequency other than a calling frequency on which the main body of the communication would take place after the initial calling.

ELEMENT III

BASIC RADIOTELEPHONE

ALTERNATING AND DIRECT CURRENT

Q. 3.01. By what other expression may a "difference of potential" be described?

A. See Q. 3.01.

Q. 3.02. By what other expression may an "electric current flow" be described?

A. See Q. 3.02.

Q. 3.03. Explain the relationship between the physical structure of the atom and electrical current flow.

A. See Q. 3.239.

Q. 3.04. With respect to electrons, what is the difference between conductors and non-conductors?

A. See Q. 3.239.

Q. 3.05. What is the difference between electrical power and electrical energy? In what units is each expressed?

A. See Q. 3.234.

Q. 3.06. What is the relationship between impedance and admittance? Between resistance and conductance?

A. Admittance (Y) is the reciprocal of Impedance (Z)
Conductance (G) is the reciprocal of Resistance (R)

D. Impedance may be defined as, "the total opposition to current flow in alternating current circuits," and is expressed by the symbol "Z." The impedance of a circuit may contain, resistance, inductive reactance and capacitive reactance. For a series circuit, impedance may be found from the equation:

$$Z = \sqrt{R^2 + (X_L - X_C)^2}$$

and is expressed in ohms

Admittance is $\dfrac{1}{Z}$ or Y. Admittance is used as a convenience in analyzing parallel a–c circuits and is expressed in mhos. For a parallel a–c circuit the admittance may be found from the equation:

$$Y = \sqrt{G^2 + B^2}$$

where, Y = Admittance in mhos
        G = Conductance in mhos
        B = Susceptance (reciprocal of reactance) in mhos

Note that the susceptance of an inductance is negative and that of a capacitance is positive. These signs are opposite to the situation when handled as reactances.

For resistance and conductance, see Q. 3.24 and 3.36.

Q. 3.07. A relay with a coil resistance of 500 ohms is designed to operate when a current of 0.2 ampere flows through the coil. What value of resistance must be connected in series with the coil if it is to be energized by a 110 volt dc source?

A. See Q. 3.508.

Q. 3.08. Draw a circuit composed of a 12 volt battery with 3 resistors (10, 120, and 300 ohms respectively) arranged in a "pi" network.
   (a) What is the total current; the current through each resistor?
   (b) What is the voltage across each resistor?
   (c) What power is dissipated in each resistor; the total power dissipated by the circuit?

A. See the figure.

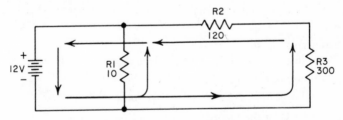

Fig. 3.08.   A "pi"-network battery circuit.

   (a) (1) Total current (I_T) = 1.23 amperes.
        (2) Current through R1 (I_{R1}) = 1.2 amperes.
        (3) Current through R2 (I_{R2}) = .0286 ampere.
        (4) Current through R3 (I_{R3}) = .0286 ampere.
   (b) (1) Voltage across R1 (E_{R1}) = 12 volts.
        (2) Voltage across R2 (E_{R2}) = 3.43 volts.
        (3) Voltage across R3 (E_{R3}) = 8.58 volts.

(c) (1) Power dissipated in R1 (P_{R1}) = 14.4 watts.
     (2) Power dissipated in R2 (P_{R2}) = 0.0978 watt.
     (3) Power dissipated in R3 (P_{R3}) = 0.245 watt.
     (4) Total power dissipated (P_T) = 14.743 watts.

D. Part (a)(1) of the question.

Step 1: Find the total resistance (R_T) across the battery

$$R_T = \frac{R1 \times (R2 + R3)}{R1 + (R2 + R3)} = \frac{10 \times (120 + 300)}{10 + (120 + 300)} = \frac{4200}{430} = 9.76 \text{ ohms}$$

Step 2: Find the total current (I_T).

$$I_T = \frac{E}{R_T} = \frac{12}{9.76} = 1.23 \text{ amperes}$$

Part (a)(2) of the question.

$$I_{R1} = \frac{E}{R1} = \frac{12}{10} = 1.2 \text{ amperes}$$

Part (a)(3) of the question.
Step 1: Find the series current through R2 and R3.

$$I_{R2, \ R3} = \frac{E}{R2 + R3} = \frac{12}{420} = .0286 \text{ ampere}$$

Step 2: Find the current through R2 (I_{R2}) which is the series current, or .0286 ampere.

Part (a)(4) of the question.
The current through R3 (I_{R3}) is also the series current, or .0286 ampere.

Part (b)(1) of the question.
The voltage across R1 (E_{R1}) is the battery voltage = 12 volts.

Part (b)(2) of the question.
$E_{R2} = I_{R2} \times R_2 = .0286 \times 120 = 3.43$ volts.

Part (b)(3) of the question.
$E_{R3} = I_{R3} \times R_3 = .0286 \times 300 = 8.58$ volts.

Part (c)(1) of the question.
The power dissipated in R1(P_{R1}) is
$P_{R1} = E \times I_{R1} = 12 \times 1.2 = 14.4$ watts.

Part (c)(2) of the question.
The power dissipated in R2(P_{R2}) is
$P_{R2} = E_{R2} \times I_{R2} = 3.42 \times .0286 = .0978$ watts or 97.8 milliwatts.

Part (c)(3) of the question.

The power dissipated in R3(P_{R3}) is
$$P_{R3} = E_{R3} \times I_{R3} = 8.58 \times .0286 = 0.245 \text{ watt.}$$

Part (c)(4) of the question.
The total power (P_T) dissipated by the circuit is the sum of the power dissipated in each resistor, or
$$P_T = P_{R1} + P_{R2} + P_{R3} = 14.4 + 0.0978 + 0.245 = 14.743 \text{ watts.}$$

Q. 3.09. Draw a circuit composed of a voltage source of 100 volts —1000 cps, a 1-microfarad capacitor in series with the source, followed by a "T" network composed of a 2-millihenry inductor, a 100-ohm resistor and a 4-millihenry inductor. The load resistor is 200 ohms.

(a) What is the total current; the current through each circuit element?

(b) What is the voltage across each circuit element?

(c) What "apparent" power is being consumed by the circuit?

(d) What real or actual power is being consumed by the circuit; by the 200 ohm resistor?

A.   See Fig. 3.09(a).

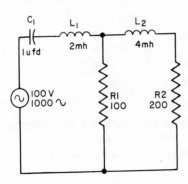

Fig. 3.09(a). "T" network and load connected to an a–c generator.

1. The total current (I_T) = 0.63 ampere.
2. The current through C1 and L1 (I_T) = 0.63 ampere.
3. The current through R1 (I_1) = 0.43 ampere.
4. The current through L2 and R2 (I_2) = 0.21 ampere.
5. The voltage across C1 (E_{C1}) = 100.17 volts.
6. The voltage across L1 (E_{L1}) = 7.91 volts.
7. The voltage across R1 (E_{R1}) = 42.65 volts.
8. The voltage across L2 (E_{L2}) = 5.27 volts.
9. The voltage across R2 (E_{R2}) = 42 volts.
10. The apparent power = 63 watts.

11. The real power = 27.03 watts.

12. The power consumed by the 200 ohm resistor = 8.8 watts.

D. The solution of this problem requires the use of complex numbers. While there are a fairly large number of steps in its solution; these proceed in logical sequence and are not difficult to follow.

(A). The first answer required is to find the total current (I_T). However, in order to accomplish this, the total equivalent impedance (Z_T) must first be computed. This is the equivalent series impedance of all the circuit elements shown in Figure 3.09(a). Thus, the series equivalent impedance of C_1 and L_1 is added vectorially to the series equivalent impedance of R1, R2 and L2 to provide Z_T.

Step 1: Find the equivalent series impedance (Z_p) of R1, R2 and L2.

$$Z_p = \frac{Z1\ Z2}{Z1 + Z2}$$

Expressed as complex numbers; first in rectangular form, we have

$$Z_p = \frac{(100 + j\theta) \times (200 + jX_{L2})}{(100 + j\theta) + (200 + jX_{L2})}$$

We must find X_{L2}

$$X_{L2} = 2\pi fL2 = 6.28 \times 1000 \times 4 \times 10^{-3} = 25.12 \text{ ohms}$$

$$Z_p = \frac{(100 + j\theta) \times (200 + j25.12)}{(100 + j\theta) + (200 + j25.12)} = \frac{20,000 + j2,512}{300 + j25.12}$$

In order to reduce this fraction, both numerator and denominator must be expressed in the polar form.

Step 2: Change the numerator to polar form.

$$\tan \theta = \frac{X}{R} = \frac{2512}{20,000} = .125$$

$$\theta = 7.1°$$

$$Z \text{ (numerator)} = \frac{X}{\sin\theta} = \frac{2512}{0.1236} = 20,323 \underline{/7.1°}$$

Step 3: Change the denominator to polar form.

$$\tan \theta = \frac{X}{R} = \frac{25.12}{300} = .084$$

$$\theta = 4.8°$$

$$Z \text{ (denominator)} = \frac{X}{\sin\theta} = \frac{25.12}{.0837} = 300.12 \text{ ohms}$$

Therefore, in polar form

$$Z_p = \frac{20{,}323 \; \underline{/7.1^\circ}}{300.12 \; \underline{/4.8^\circ}} = 67.7 \; \underline{/2.6^\circ}$$

(B). It is now necessary to determine the equivalent impedance (Z_s) of C1 and L1.

Step 1: Find the reactance of C1

$$X_{C1} = \frac{1}{2\pi f C1} = \frac{0.159}{1000 \times 1 \times 10^{-6}} = 159 \text{ ohms}$$

Step 2: Find the reactance of L1

$$X_{L1} = 2\pi f L1 = 6.28 \times 1000 \times 2 \times 10^{-3} = 12.56 \text{ ohms}$$

Step 3: Find the combined impedance (Z_s) of C1 and L1

$$Z_s = 12.56 - 159 = -146.44 \text{ ohms (capacitive)}$$

(C). The next step is to combine Z_p and Z_s vectorially to find Z_T, which is the actual load on the generator. With the aid of Z_T, we may determine the generator current (I_T) and then the remainder of the answers to this problem.

Step 1: $Z_T = Z_p + Z_s$
$\quad\quad\quad Z_T = 67.7 \; \underline{/2.6^\circ} + (0 - j146.44)$

To perform this addition, Z_p must first be converted to rectangular form

$\quad\quad\quad Z_p = 67.7 \; (\cos. \; 2.6^\circ + j \sin 2.6^\circ)$
$\quad\quad\quad Z_p = 67.7 \; (0.9990 + j0.0454) = 67.63 + j3.07$, and
$\quad\quad\quad Z_T = (67.63 + j3.07) + (0 \; -j146.44) = 67.63 \; -j143.37$

Step 2: It is now necessary to convert the rectangular form of Z_T (above) to its polar form

$$\tan \theta = \frac{X_c}{R} = \frac{143.37}{67.63}$$

$$\tan \theta = 2.1$$

$$\theta = -64.6^\circ$$

$$Z_T = \frac{X}{\sin \theta} = \frac{143.37}{\sin 64.6^\circ} = \frac{143.37}{0.9033} = 158.7 \text{ ohms}$$

Z_T in polar form $= 158.7 \; \underline{/-64.6^\circ}$

(D). Find the total current (I_T).

$$I_T = \frac{E}{Z_T} = \frac{100}{158.7} = 0.63 \text{ ampere}$$

(E). Find the current through C1 and L1. This is the same as I_T, or 0.63 ampere.

(F). Find the currents I1 and I2 (See Figure 3.09(b)).

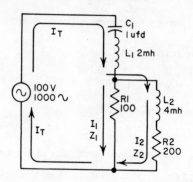

Fig. 3.09(b). The diagram is redrawn here for clarity in solving the problem.

Step 1: Find the voltage (E_p) across the parallel branch (Z_p) composed of R1 and R2, L2.

$$E_p = I_T \times Z_p = 0.63 \times 67.7 = 42.65 \text{ volts.}$$

Step 2: $I1 = \dfrac{E_p}{Z_1} = \dfrac{42.65}{100} = 0.43 \text{ ampere}$

Step 3: $I2 = \dfrac{E_p}{Z2}$

We must find the value of Z2, which is the vector sum of X_{L2} and R2 in series.

$$Z2 = \sqrt{(R2)^2 + (X_{L2})^2} = \sqrt{(200)^2 + (25.12)^2} = 201.5 \text{ ohms}$$

$$I2 = \frac{42.65}{201.5} = 0.21 \text{ ampere}$$

This is the current in L2 and R2

(G). We are now ready to find the voltages across each circuit element. (The voltage across R1 is the same as E_p, or 42.65 volts.)

Step 1: Find the voltage across L2

$$E_{L2} = I2 \times X_{L2} = 0.21 \times 25.12 = 5.27 \text{ volts.}$$

Step 2: Find the voltage across R2

$$E_{R2} = I2 \times R2 = 0.21 \times 200 = 42 \text{ volts.}$$

Step 3: Find the voltage across C1

$$E_{C1} = I_T \times X_{C1} = 0.63 \times 159 = 100.17 \text{ volts.}$$

Step 4: Find the voltage across L1.

$$E_{L1} = I_T \times X_{L1} = 0.63 \times 12.56 = 7.91 \text{ volts.}$$

Note: It may appear that the individual voltages add up to more than the generator voltage. However, these are out of phase and must be added vectorially.

(H). Find the apparent power (P_a) consumed by the circuit.

$$P_a = E \times I_T = 100 \times 0.63 = 63 \text{ volt-amperes.}$$

(I). Find the real power consumed by the circuit (P_R)

$$P_R = E \times I_T \times \cos \theta \ (64.6°) = 100 \times 0.63 \times 0.4289 = 27.03 \text{ watts}$$

(J). Find the power consumed by the 200 ohm resistor, R2

$$P_{R2} = I2^2 \times R2 = (0.21)^2 \times 200 = .044 \times 200 = 8.8 \text{ watts.}$$

Q. 3.10. What is the relationship between wire size and resistance of the wire?

A. See Q. 3.05, 3.12, 3.13, 3.227.

Q. 3.11. What is "skin effect"? How does it affect the resistance of conductors at the higher radio frequencies?

A. See Q. 3.319.

Q. 3.12. Why is impedance matching between electrical devices an important factor? Is it always to be desired? Can it always be attained in practice?

A. (a) Impedance matching is important in certain cases in order to effect maximum transfer of power, minimum VSWR (on transmission lines) and consequently a reasonably flat frequency response of a line (within the practical design limits).

(b) Impedance matching is not always desirable, as is the case in some amplifiers.

(c) Perfect impedance matching is not always attained in practice since the magnitude and phase angle of the impedances must be matched. However, from a practical standpoint and utilizing a given frequency band of operation, satisfactory impedance matching may be achieved. See also Q. 4.22.

Q. 3.13. A loudspeaker with an impedance of 4 ohms is working in a plate circuit which has an impedance of 4000 ohms. What is the im-

pedance ratio of an output transformer used to match the plate circuit to the speaker? What is the turns ratio?

A. (a) The impedance ratio is 1000 to 1.
(b) The turns ratio is 31.6 to 1.

D. Let the plate circuit impedance equal Z_p (primary impedance). Let the loudspeaker impedance equal Z_s (secondary impedance). The impedance ratio is

$$\frac{Z_p}{Z_s} = \frac{4000}{4} = 1000 \text{ to } 1$$

A basic (approximate) formula relating impedance ratio and turns ratio is:

$$\frac{N_p}{N_s} = \sqrt{\frac{Z_p}{Z_s}}, \text{ or } \left(\frac{N_p}{N_s}\right)^2 = \frac{Z_p}{Z_s}$$

where; N_p is the number of turns in the primary.
N_s is the number of turns in the secondary.
Z_p is the primary impedance.
Z_s is the secondary impedance.
From the above, the turns ratio is found by,

$$\frac{N_p}{N_s} = \sqrt{\frac{Z_p}{Z_s}} = \sqrt{\frac{4000}{4}} = 31.6$$

See also Q. 4.15, 4.16, 6.266, 6.267, 6.268, 6.269.

Q. 3.14. Compare some properties of electrostatic and electromagnetic fields.

A. (1) If two conductors are separated by an insulator and a difference of potential applied between the two conductors, it can be shown that electric energy is stored between the two conductors. This energy is said to exist in an electrostatic field between (mainly) the conductors. If the charging source is removed, the charge (or energy) remains as before and we have a charged capacitor, which stores potential energy in its field. The amount of energy stored is expressed by the equation

$$W = \tfrac{1}{2}CE^2 \text{ joules}$$

where   C = capacitance in farads
E = charging potential in volts
W = energy of the electrostatic field in joules (watt-seconds)

The lines of electrostatic force between two unlike charges (corresponding to magnetic lines of force) are depicted in Fig. 3.14.

The directional arrows on the lines show the direction of force on an electron placed in the field. The electron would be attracted by the positive charge and repelled by the negative charge. Coulomb's law is useful in describing the electrostatic field. This law states that the force be-

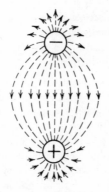

Fig. 3.14. Electrostatic field between unlike charges.

tween two charges is proportional to the product of the charges and inversely proportional to the square of the distance between them. In Fig. 3.14, if a dielectric material was placed between the unlike charges, some of the electrons in the dielectric would be attracted toward the positive charge and potential energy would now be stored in the dielectric. This process is called "electrostatic induction" and corresponds to the induction caused by an electromagnetic field.

(2) If a current of electricity is passed through a wire (or coil), it will be found that an electromagnetic field will build up to a maximum value in the space surrounding the wire. A certain amount of electrical energy will exist in this electromagnetic field and may be expressed by the equation

$$W = \frac{1}{2}LI^2$$

where   L = inductance in henries
        I = current in amperes
        W = energy of the electromagnetic field in joules
            (watt-seconds)

Unlike the electrostatic field, if the current is cut off, the electromagnetic field shortly ceases to exist; the energy being returned to the wire (or coil). (In actuality, there is always stray capacity across the inductance. Thus, when the excitation is cut off, the energy creates damped oscillations of this tuned circuit.) Since the electromagnetic field requires a current flow to exist, the energy involved is kinetic energy.

If a conductor is moved through the magnetic field (but not parallel to it) magnetic induction will take place and a current will be caused to flow in the conductor. Similarly, if the excitation of the original wire (or coil) is varied, a current will be induced into a stationary wire or coil. In this case, the electromagnetic field is caused to move past the wire and the moving field induces a secondary current. Note an important distinction between electrostatic and electromagnetic fields. An electrostatic field (kinetic energy) may cause induction while stationary. Conversely, an electromagnetic field (or the secondary conductor) must be in motion to produce induction.

D.   It is important to note that a radiated wave from a transmitting antenna (or other radiator) is composed of both electrostatic and electromagnetic fields. The total energy content of the wave is constant over one cycle. However, the two fields are 90° apart in phase (as well as in space) and the energy is continuously interchanged between the electrostatic and electromagnetic fields. In the case of a vertical radiator (vertically polarized) the electrostatic lines of force are situated mainly in the vertical plane and the electromagnetic lines of force are mainly in the horizontal plane. For maximum efficiency of a receiving antenna for this wave, the receiving antenna should also be vertical. In this case the maximum induced electrostatic and electromagnetic field energy will occur in the receiving antenna.

Q. 3.15.   In what way are electrical properties of common circuit elements effected by electromagnetic fields? Are interstage connecting leads susceptible to these fields?

A.   1. The independent electrical properties of circuit elements are not affected by electromagnetic fields. However, the performance of electrical circuits is sometimes affected by the coupling of electromagnetic fields into common circuit elements, such as, coils capacitors and vacuum tubes. Such coupling may (depending on phase relationships) cause oscillation and/or bandwidth problems. It may also result in such conditions as hum pickup.

2. Interstage connecting leads may pick up electromagnetic fields and cause problems similar to those mentioned above.

D.   In the design of electronic circuits, particularly where high-gain stages are involved, one of the most important considerations is the prevention of undesired coupling between stages of the circuitry. As mentioned above, such coupling (or undesired feedback) may be of such phase as to reinforce the signal appearing at an earlier stage. This can cause instability, regeneration, oscillation and/or a reduction of bandwidth of the circuit. Such undesired coupling can be simple induced currents into common circuit elements, or into inter- or intra-stage wiring. In some situations, the coupling may be through the route of the metal chassis itself. It it not possible in this book to present detailed design information for the avoidance of this condition. However, some of the more common design precautions are:

(1) Shielding of glass vacuum tubes in critical circuits.

(2) Shielding of selected input or output leads wherever possible and desirable.

(3) Shielding of coils and/or of entire stages which may be susceptible to feedback problems.

(4) Restriction of the gain of each critical stage to reduce the magnitude of feedback.

(5) Shielding the entire bottom of the chassis to eliminate pick up
of stray adjacent fields.

(6) Use of special circuit grounding procedures, such as all grid-circuit returns to one ground and all plate-circuit returns to another ground,
or at least to another portion of the metal chassis.

(7) Use of adequate decoupling circuits between stages, including
such items as filament-circuit chokes and plate and grid-decoupling RC
circuits.

Q. 3.16. **Which factors determine the amplitude of the emf induced
in a conductor which is cutting magnetic lines of force?**

A.   See Question 3.03.

Q. 3.17.   Define the term "reluctance."

A.   See Question 3.62.

**Q. 3.18.   In what way does an inductance affect the voltage-current
phase relationship of a circuit? Why is the phase of a circuit important?**

A.   (a) See Q. 6.94.

(b) Phase may be important for various reasons depending upon the
application of the circuit. For example, in power circuits, phase angle
determines the power factor. In color TV receivers the correct phase of
the demodulation signals is vital to insure proper color reproduction.
For other examples, see the discussion.

D.   Several other cases where phase is important to the circuitry
involved are:

(1) Operation of two or three phase motors.

(2) Operation of servo systems.

(3) Correct speaker and circuit phasing in stereophonic audio systems.

(4) Synchronization of TV and FM multiplex signals at both transmitter and receiver.

(5) Aircraft navigational receivers.

There are numerous other examples where phasing is important. However, there are also many circuits where phasing is not important. For
example:

(1) Broadcast receivers and transmitters.

(2) Ordinary FM receivers.

(3) Single channnel amplifiers.

(4) Power supplies.

(5) Many types of test equipment.

Q. 3.19. Draw two cycles of a sine-wave on a graph of amplitude versus time. Assume a frequency of 5 mc/s.

(a) What would be the wave length of one cycle in meters; in centimeters?

(b) How many degrees does one cycle represent?

(c) How much time would it take for the wave to "rotate" 45°; 90°; 280°?

(d) If there were a second harmonic of this frequency, how many cycles thereof would be represented on this graph?

(e) On the same graph draw two cycles of another sine-wave leading the first by 45°.

(f) What would be the velocity of this wave or any other electromagnetic wave in free space?

A.   See the figure.

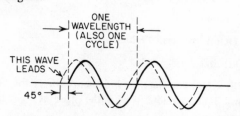

Fig. 3.19. Two cycles of two sine waves, one leading the other by 45 degrees.

(a)(1) Wavelength in meters = 60 meters.

(2) Wavelength in centimeters = 6000 centimeters.

(b) One cycle represents 360 degrees.

(c)(1) The wave will rotate 45 degrees in .025 microsecond.

(2) The wave will rotate 90 degrees in .05 microsecond.

(3) The wave will rotate 280 degrees in 0.155 microsecond.

(d) The second harmonic would be represented by 4 cycles.

(e) See the figure.

(f) The velocity would be 300,000,000 meters per second.

D.   (a) The wavelength of one cycle in meters is,

$$\lambda = \frac{300}{f(mc)} = \frac{300}{5} = 60 \text{ meters}$$

The wavelength in centimeters is,

$$\lambda \text{ (cm)} = \frac{300}{f(mc)} \times 100 = \frac{30,000}{5} = 6,000 \text{ cm.}$$

Note: In common usage, centimeters are used to describe wavelengths at much higher frequencies. For example at 10,000 mc, the wavelength is 3 cm. This is a matter of convenient notation.

(b) One cycle represents 360°; since it may be considered to be derived from a vector rotating inside of a 360 degree circle.

(c)(1) The wave will rotate 45° in $\frac{1}{8}\left(\frac{45}{360}\right)$ of the time required for one complete cycle, which is,

$$T \text{ (sec)} = \frac{1}{F(cycles)}$$

$$T \text{ (microsec)} = \frac{1}{F \text{ (megacycles)}}$$

$$= \frac{1}{5} \text{ or } 0.2 \text{ microsec for one complete cycle.}$$

For 45°, $T = \frac{0.2}{8} = .025$ microsec.

(2) The wave will rotate 90° (¼ cycle) in

$$T = \frac{0.2}{4} = .05 \text{ microsecond.}$$

(3) The wave will rotate 280° in

$$T = 0.2 \times \frac{280}{360} = 0.155 \text{ microsecond}$$

(d) The second harmonic would be 10 megacycles, each cycle occupying ½ the time of a 5 megacycle wave. Therefore 4 cycles of the second harmonic would be shown on the graph.

(e) See the figure.

(f) The velocity of any electromagnetic wave in free space is 300,-000,000 meters per second.

Q. 3.20. Explain how to determine the sum of two equal vector quantities having the same reference point but whose directions are 90° apart; 0° apart; 180° apart? How does this pertain to electrical currents or voltages?

A. (1) This may be accomplished by graphical means or by trigonometry. (See Discussion).

(2) Electrical currents or voltages are frequently represented by vector quantities in the solution of electrical problems.

D. (1) Two forces (or quantities) acting simultaneously on the same reference point may be summed and replaced by a single quantity. This single quantity will produce the same effect on the reference point, as the two individual quantities. The two initial quantities being added are vectors. That is, they have both magnitude and direction. The resultant of the two vectors will also be a vector and must be expressed in magnitude and direction. Two vectors 90° apart are illustrated in Fig. 3.20.

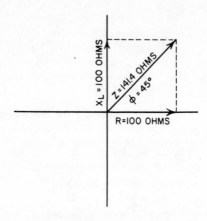

Fig. 3.20. Illustrating the solution of two vectors which are 90 degrees apart.

In order for this example to have the greatest meaning, quantities involving actual electrical elements are used. Thus the figure shows a resistance of 100 ohms and an inductive reactance of 100 ohms at right angles and as they are normally depicted in graphical form. The resultant quantity (Z) will be the impedance of a series circuit of the two elements. The determination of the sum of R and X_L may be done graphically, that is, by drawing figure 3.20 to any convenient scale and measuring the magnitude and direction (phase angle) of Z. The more usual method is by means of a common trigonometric theorum which yields the equation

$$Z = \sqrt{R^2 + X_L^2} = \sqrt{100^2 + 100^2} = 141.4 \text{ ohms}$$

The direction (phase angle) is

$$\theta = \tan^{-1} \frac{X_L}{R} = \tan^{-1} 1$$

$$\theta = 45 \text{ degrees}$$

(2) Two vector quantities which are 0 degrees apart (in phase) are simply added arithmetically. The direction remains unchanged.

(3) Two vectors which are 180 degrees apart (180 degrees out of phase) are added algebraically. For example if vector #1 equals + 100 and vector #2 equals −150, the resultant is 100 − 150 = −50.

(4) A vector may represent any type of quantity having both magnitude and direction. In electrical circuits, there is no physical direction involved. However, there is frequently the problem of phase angle. A typical example of a phase angle has been given in this discussion. (See also Q. 3.09, 3.18 and 3.19, above.) Generally, the problem of most frequent interest is the phase angle between the voltage and current in a circuit. In the solution of electrical problems, vectors are commonly employed and the student should acquire a working knowledge of vectors and complex numbers.

Q. 3.21.   Explain how the values of resistance and capacitance in an RC network affect its time constant. How would the output waveform be affected by the frequency of the input in an RC network?

A.   (1) The charging time is determined by the value of the capacitor and resistor in the circuit and both of these elements directly affect the time constant. Assuming R and C to be in series with the d–c supply voltage; if the resistor is increased in value, the charging current is reduced. This increases the time required to charge the capacitor to any given voltage level. On the other hand, increasing the value of capacitance (storage tank) with a fixed resistor, requires the current (which is limited by the resistor) to flow for a greater period of time.

(2) If the waveform is a sine wave, the shape of the wave is unaffected by the RC network, regardless of its frequency. However, the amplitude of the output waveform may be reduced as the frequency is reduced below certain limits. See also Q. 4.170.

Q. 3.22.   Explain how the values of resistance and inductance in an RL network affect its time constant.

A. The time constant of an RL network is defined as the time (in seconds) required for the current to reach 63.2% of its maximum possible value. An increase in the value of inductance will directly increase the time constant. This is true because an inductance tends to resist any change of current and this property is directly proportional to the value of inductance. However, unlike the RC case, an increase of resistance will actually decrease the time constant. The reason an increase of resistance causes a decrease of the RL time constant is that the magnitude of the current at any given time is reduced. A reduced current results in a lesser rate of change of current at any given time. Since the rate of change of current determines the counter emf and therefore the opposition to current flow, a lesser rate permits the current to rise faster; hence a shorter time constant is attained. Of course, the converse is also true and a smaller resistance will result in a longer time constant for an RL circuit.

D.   The time constant of an RL circuit may be found by the equation

$$T = \frac{L}{R} \text{ seconds, where}$$

L = inductance in henries
R = total series resistance in ohms (including the resistance of the inductance).

When the charging circuit is opened, the time constant of an RL circuit is changed. Assuming current had been at a maximum in the coil when the source was instantaneously disconnected, the energy in the coil is dissipated in the resistance of an oscillating circuit consisting of the coil (with its inherent resistance), the stray capacity of the circuit and the coil itself.

Q. 3.23.   Explain the theory of molecular alignment as it affects magnetic properties of materials.

A.   The theory of molecular alignment is based on the assumption that magnetic materials contain tiny molecular magnets called "magnetic dipoles." If the dipoles are caused to be in alignment, with like poles all pointing the same way, the material is said to be magnetized. In this case magnetic North and South poles appear at opposite ends of the magnetic material.

D.   In soft magnetic metals, the molecular alignment must be maintained by an electric current (electromagnet). When the current is removed the alignment becomes largely random and only a small "residual" magnetism remains. Iron is a soft magnetic material. However, there are certain hard magnetic materials, such as Cobalt or Alnico. When these are magnetized, they retain their magnetism indefinitely, if given proper care. It is assumed that in this case the molecular structure of the material is such that it is difficult for the magnetic dipoles to be moved from their aligned position. Such "permanent" magnets can be weakened or demagnetized by being subjected to mechanical shock, excessive heat, or an electromagnetic field which opposes the magnetization of the permanent magnet.

Q. 3.24.   What is the relationship between the inductance of a coil and the number of turns of wire in the coil; the permeability of the core material used?

A.   (a) See Question 3.61.

(b) The inductance of a coil varies directly with the permeability of the core. See also Q. 3.22.

D. The permeability of a substance is the ratio of magnetic flux density in that substance to the field strength which produces it.

Permeability is a property of a material which is somewhat analogous magnetically to conductivity in an electric circuit. If a magnetic field of strength "H" exists in a certain space, and the space is then filled with a permeable material, the new field intensity will be $B = uH$, where "u" is the permeability of the material.

Q. 3.25. What factors influence the direction of magnetic lines of force produced by an electromagnet?

A. See Q. 3.21.

Q. 3.26. Explain how self and mutual inductance produce transformer action.

A. When current flows through the primary winding of a transformer, the self inductance of the primary causes a counter emf to appear across it because of the expanding magnetic field around the primary. (With a sine wave input into the primary, the primary magnetic field is continuously expanding and contracting at the frequency of the sine wave.) The expanding (or contracting) magnetic field not only affects the primary, but also cuts across the secondary winding of the transformer. This causes a voltage to be induced into the secondary winding by mutual inductance and a current to flow in the secondary winding, if a load is connected across it.

D. The mutual inductance of a transformer may be calculated from the equation

$$M = K \sqrt{L1L2} \text{ henries,}$$

where M = mutual inductance in henries
  K = coefficient of coupling (See Q. 3.27 below) between the coils.
  $L1$ and $L2$ = values of self inductance of the two coils.

In practice, the mutual inductance may be greatly increased by winding the inductances on some form of iron core. This has the effect of increasing the coefficient of coupling greatly, since the magnetic flux generated by the primary will be confined to a large extent by the iron core and will therefore link the secondary winding more completely.

Q. 3.27. What does coefficient of coupling mean?

A. The coefficient of coupling is a number (usually a decimal) which defines the ratio of the amount of magnetic flux linking a secondary coil, as compared to the original magnetix flux generated in the primary coil.

D. Coefficient of coupling is expressed by the equation

$$K = \frac{M}{\sqrt{L1L2}}$$

where

K = coefficient of coupling (a decimal)
M = mutual inductance of the two coils
L1 and L2 = self inductances of the two coils.

The coefficient of coupling may be increased by one or more of several possible expedients:

1. Placing the windings closer together.
2. Winding the primary and secondary wires adjacent to one another (bi-filar winding).
3. Winding the coils on a common iron core.

Where all the flux generated by one coil links the second coil, the value of K = 1. However, typical values of K are .05 to 0.3 for air-core coils and K may approach unity for common wound iron-core coils.

Q. 3.28. How does the capacitance of a capacitor vary with area of plates; spacing between plates; dielectric material between plates?

A. See Questions 3.16, and 3.15.

Q. 3.29. Assuming the voltage on a capacitor is at or below the maximum allowable value, does the value of the capacitor have any relationship to the amount of charge it can store? What relationship does this storage of charges have to the total capacitance of two or more capacitors in series; in parallel?

A. See Questions 3.57, 3.18, 3.52, 3.51, 3.54, and 3.58.

Q. 3.30. How should electrolytic capacitors be connected in a circuit in relation to polarity? Which type of low leakage capacitor is used most often in transmitters?

A. See Q. 3.258.

Where large values are required, oil-filled paper dielectric capacitors are frequently used. For smaller values of capacitance, mica and ceramic dielectric capacitors are frequently used.

Q. 3.31. A certain power company charges 7¢ per kilowatt-hour. How much would it cost to operate three 120 volt lamp bulbs, connected in parallel, each having an internal resistance of 100 ohms, for 24 hours?

A. The cost would be 73 cents.

D. Step 1: Find the power used by each bulb.

$$P = \frac{E^2}{R} = \frac{14,400}{100} = 144 \text{ watts}$$

Step 2: The power used by three bulbs is $144 \times 3 = 432$ watts.

Step 3: Find the watt-hours for the three bulbs. This is $432 \times 24 = 10,368$ watt-hours.

Step 4: To find the kilowatt hours, divide the watt-hours by 1000, or $\frac{10,368}{1000} = 10.368$ kilowatt hours (kwh).

Step 5: To find the cost, multiply the total kwh by the unit cost per kwh, or $10.368 \times .07 = 73$ cents.

Q. 3.32. The output of an amplifier stage having a voltage gain of 30 db is 25 volts. What is the input voltage level?

A. The input voltage level = 0.79 volts.

D. See Q. 3.38 and 4.125.

Q. 3.33. What is the impedance of a parallel circuit which is composed of a pure inductance and a pure capacitance at resonance; of a series circuit at resonance?

A. See Questions 3.323 and 3.322.

Q. 3.34. What is the "Q" of a circuit? How is it affected by the circuit resistance? How does the "Q" of a circuit affect bandwidth?

A. See Q. 4.168 and 4.169.

Q. 3.35. Draw a circuit diagram of a low-pass filter composed of a "constant-k" and an "m-derived" section.

A. See the figure.

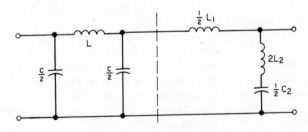

Fig. 3.35. Low-pass filter, composed of a "constant-k" section (left of dotted line) and an "m-derived" section (right of dotted line).

D. Both the "constant-k" and "m-derived" filters are special cases of the basic filters shown in Figure 3.36. Basically, such filters are used to achieve sharper attenuation characteristics. The "m-derived" section is known as the "series-derived" type. There is also a "shunt-derived" type (not shown) where C_2 would be eliminated from the shunt arm and placed across L_1. The "constant-k" section shown is a pi section. Design data for such filters may be found in Electrical Engineering text books.

Filters are designed to operate into a resistive terminating impedance. When this is true, the impedance looking into the input of the filter has the same impedance value throughout most of the filter pass-band. This constant impedance property (over the pass band) is more readily achieved by using "m-derived" and "constant-k" filters than with simple filters.

Q. 3.36. In general, why are filters used? Why are "band-stop," "high-pass," and "low-pass" filters used? Draw schematic diagrams of the most commonly used filters.

A. (1) In general, the purpose of a filter is to select the desired frequency component(s) (from a complex input wave); to reject the undesired frequency component(s) and to apply only the desired component(s) to the circuit(s) where they are required. (This is an idealistic definition, since in practice, some portion of the undesired frequency components will also be present at the output of the filter.)

(2) A "band-stop" (also called "band suppression," or "band exclusion") filter is one which discriminates against a band of frequencies within a spectrum and which passess frequencies above and below this band.

(3) A "high-pass" filter is one which permits all frequencies above a selected cut-off frequency to be passed without attenuation and rejects frequencies below the cut-off frequency.

(4) A "low-pass" filter is one which permits all frequencies below a selected cut-off frequency to be passed without attenuation and rejects frequencies above the cut-off frequency.

(5) Schematic diagrams of commonly used filters are given in the figure. The most commonly used types are known as, "L," "T," and "PI" filters. These may be used in single sections or in multiple sections to provide the desired filtering action. In addition to these, there are various other types of filters which provide special filter-response characteristics when needed. Among the other types are the "constant-k" and "m-derived" types, which are shown in Q. 3.35, above.

Q. 3.37. Name four materials that make good insulators at low frequencies, but not at UHF, or above.

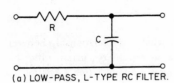

(a) LOW-PASS, L-TYPE RC FILTER.

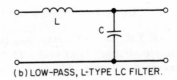

(b) LOW-PASS, L-TYPE LC FILTER.

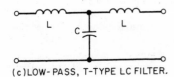

(c) LOW-PASS, T-TYPE LC FILTER.

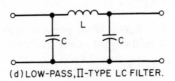

(d) LOW-PASS, Π-TYPE LC FILTER.

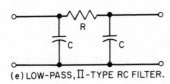

(e) LOW-PASS, Π-TYPE RC FILTER.

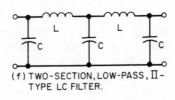

(f) TWO-SECTION, LOW-PASS, Π-TYPE LC FILTER.

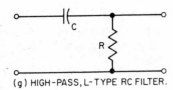

(g) HIGH-PASS, L-TYPE RC FILTER.

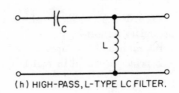

(h) HIGH-PASS, L-TYPE LC FILTER.

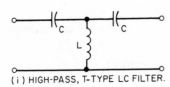

(i) HIGH-PASS, T-TYPE LC FILTER.

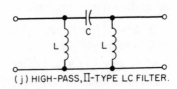

(j) HIGH-PASS, Π-TYPE LC FILTER.

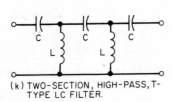

(k) TWO-SECTION, HIGH-PASS, T-TYPE LC FILTER.

Fig. 3.36. Common types of filters.

A. See Q. 3.11.

Q. 3.38. In an iron-core transformer, what is the relationship between the transformer turns ratio and primary to secondary current ratio; between turns ratio and primary to seconday voltage ratio? (Assume no losses).

A. See Questions 3.318, 6.266, 6.267, 6.268, and 4.15.

Q. 3.39. What prevents high currents from flowing in the primary of an unloaded power transformer?

A. The relatively high value of inductive reactance of the primary winding.

D. When power is taken from the secondary, the secondary current sets up a magnetic field from this winding. Since the windings have mutual inductance, the secondary field cuts the primary winding and induces a voltage into the primary which causes additional primary current to flow. The additional current is taken from the line to supply the power requirements of the secondary. In effect, the secondary field causes a reduction of primary inductance and the smaller reactance permits additional primary current to be taken from the line.

Q. 3.40. An audio transformer has a resistive load connected across its secondary terminals. What is the relationship between this resistance, the turns ratio and the input impedance at the primary terminals? How is this principle useful in matching impedances?

A. See Q. 4.15, 4.16.
Any two impedances (within practical limits) may be matched by using the proper turns ratio of a transformer.

Q. 3.41. How is power lost in an iron-core transformer? In an air-core transformer?

A. See Q. 4.12. (See also Q. 3.11 for skin effect).
Power is dissipated through the following losses: (air core).

  a. Radiation.
  b. Skin effect.
  c. Absorption through mutual coupling and/or shield losses.
  d. Bandwidth loading resistor, where used in shunt with the coil.

Q. 3.42. Explain the operation of a *break-contact* relay; a *make-contact* relay.

A. (1) A *"break-contact"* relay is also known as a "normally-closed" relay. In this type of relay, when the coil is de-energized, one or more sets of contacts are closed and will open only when the relay coil is energized.

(2) A *"make-contact"* relay is also known as a "normally-open" relay. In this case, one or more sets of contacts remain open in the de-energized condition and close only when the relay coil is energized.

Q. 3.43. What is the value and tolerance of a resistor which is color-coded (left-to-right): RED, BLACK, ORANGE, GOLD?

A. The value of the resistor is 20,000 ohms. Gold signifies a ± 5 percent tolerance.

Q. 3.44. What would be the value, tolerance and voltage rating of an EIA mica capacitor whose first row colors were (from left-to-right): BLUE, RED, GREEN: second row: GREEN, SILVER, RED?

A. In the EIA system, six dots are used to identify the capacitor. The top three dots are read from left-to-right, but the bottom three are read from right-to-left (continuing around the loop). Thus, in the question, the colors should be read in sequence as, (1) BLUE, (2) RED, (3) GREEN, (4) RED, (5) SILVER, (6) GREEN. However, in the EIA system the first dot (1) would be white, identifying the code as that of EIA and not MIL (which would have a black first dot). Therefore, the color sequence should read instead, (1) WHITE, (2) RED, (3) GREEN, (4) RED, (5) SILVER, (6) GREEN.

The value of capacitance (in $\mu\mu$fds) is taken from dots 2, 3 and 4 and is 2500 $\mu\mu$fds.

The tolerance is taken from dot 5 (Silver) and is ± 10 percent.

Dot 6 gives the EIA class (A through G) which specifies temperature coefficient, leakage resistance and other variable factors. The voltage rating is not given by any color dot directly but is generally 500 volts. (Voltage ratings may be found in the manufacturers data sheets or in supply catalogues, when in doubt.)

EIA are the initials for the Electronic Industries Association, formerly known as the RETMA; which stood for the Radio-Electronics-Television Manufacturers Association.

Q. 3.45. List three precautions which should be taken in soldering electrical connections to assure a permanent junction.

A. Some precautions in soldering are:

1. Clean parts thoroughly, if they are not already tinned. If the parts are not tinned, it is helpful to tin then before soldering.

2. Make a good mechanical connection between the parts.

3. If the solder does not have an inner rosin core, it will be helpful to apply a small quantity of rosin to the joint. (Most electronic-type solders have an inner core of rosin or other non-corrosive flux.)

4. Use a soldering iron or soldering gun of high enough wattage rating so the joint will be adequately heated.

5. Heat the joint so it is hot enough to melt the solder. Don't "paste" molten solder on a cold joint.

6. Maintain the heat for a sufficient time to permit the solder to flow freely over the entire joint.

7. Use just enough solder to cover the entire joint evenly.

8. Never use acid flux in electrical work, as it is highly corrosive.

9. Be certain the parts of the joint do not move while the solder is cooling.

ELECTRON TUBES

Q. 3.46. Discuss the physical characteristics and a common usage of each of the following electron tube types:
   a. diode
   b. triode
   c. tetrode
   d. pentode
   e. beam power
   f. remote-cut off
   g. duo-triode
   h. cold-cathode
   i. thyratron

A. (a) Diode: A diode is a two electrode vacuum tube, containing a cathode and a plate housed in a glass or metal-evacuated envelope. Connections from the elements are brought out to a plug-in base, or to wires in the case of sub-miniature tubes. The cathode may be a directly-heated wire or an indirectly-heated metal sleeve. In the case of the sleeve, this is given an oxide coating which is an efficient electron emitter. (Directly-heated cathodes are also oxide coated to improve their emission characteristics). Indirectly-heated cathode sleeves are brought up to operating temperature by a heated filament wire inside of, but insulated from, the emitter sleeve. Diodes are rectifiers and are used as r–f detectors, peak detectors and power-supply rectifiers. They are also commonly used as d–c restorers (clampers), limiters and clippers.

(b) Triode: See Q. 3.99, 3.276. Triodes are used as oscillators, r–f and a–f amplifiers, clampers, voltage regulators and cathode followers.

(c) Tetrode: See Q. 3.100, 3.97. Tetrodes are rarely used, but may be found in some transmitters as power r–f amplifiers or modulators. Tetrode transistors are quite common.

(d) Pentode: See Q. 3.97, 6.137. Pentodes may be used as r–f and i–f amplifiers, video amplifiers and crystal oscillators.

(e) Beam Power: See Q. 3.476, 6.139.

(f) Remote Cut Off: This generally refers to pentodes only, having a special control-grid spacing. The grid turns are close together at both ends, but have a wider spacing in the center. A common application for these tubes is in AGC (or AVC) controlled i–f amplifiers. Another use would be in audio volume expander or compresser circuits. In general, they are used in circuits where an automatic (or manual) control of circuit gain is desired, by changing the control-grid voltage(s) of the stage(s).

(g) Duo-Triode: This merely indicates two triodes are contained in one tube envelope. The primary advantages are the savings in space, parts and cost. The uses are the same as given in part (b) of this question.

(h) Cold Cathode: See Q. 3.389. Common uses are as voltage regulators and rectifiers.

(i) Thyratron: See Q. 3.476.

Q. 3.47. What is the principal advantage of a tetrode tube over a triode tube as a radio-frequency amplifier?

A. See Questions 3.120, 3.97, and 3.115.

Q. 3.48. Compare tetrode tubes to triode tubes in reference to high plate current and interelectrode capacitance.

A. (1) Tetrode tubes of similar construction to triodes, are capable of higher plate currents, because the plate current is largely dependent upon a constant value of screen-grid voltage. (See Discussion).

(2) Tetrodes have greatly reduced values of control grid-to-plate capacitance compared to triodes. (See Discussion).

D. (1) Maximum plate current characteristics of tetrodes versus triodes cannot be directly compared, since this is largely a function of the permissable plate dissipation of a particular tube. However, all other conditions being equal, the affect of the screen grid operation is to make the plate current relatively independent of the plate voltage and to reduce the space charge in the vicinity of the plate. When the actual plate voltage of a triode is reduced because of high current through the plate load, this in turn tends to limit the maximum possible plate current. However, in the tetrode (or pentode), the plate current is more dependent upon screen-grid (than plate) voltage and may therefore be driven to a higher value, since the screen-grid voltage remains at a relatively fixed value, regardless of the plate current.

(2) In the tetrode, the screen grid is interposed between the control grid and the plate. The a–c ground of the screen grid is returned to ground or to the cathode and has the effect of an electrostatic shield between the plate and control grid. The effective grid to plate capacitance now consists of two small capacitances in series, the control grid-

to-screen grid capacitance and the screen grid-to-plate capacitance. The resultant capacitance (control grid-to-plate) is smaller than either capacitance and may be in the order of .01 $\mu\mu$fd. In comparison, a triode of similar dimensions and ratings may have a grid to plate capacitance of 2.0 $\mu\mu$fd. The lower capacitance of the tetrode greatly reduces plate to control grid feedback and consequently the possibility of sustaining oscillations or regeneration in the stage. See also Questions 3.46 and 3.47, above.

Q. 3.49.   Are there any advantages or disadvantages of filament type vacuum tubes when compared with the indirectly heated types?

A.   (1) Filament-type tubes: — Advantages.

(a) Quick heating.

(b) More efficient in converting heating power into thermal emission.

(c) Used to provide high values of current (i.e., in rectifiers, or high power tubes).

(2) Filament-type tubes: — Disadvantages.

(a) Prone to hum problems.

(b) Lower gain.

(c) Prone to filament breakage.

(d) Require higher operating temperatures for efficient emission.

(3) Indirectly-heated tubes: — Advantages.

(a) Elimination of heater hum problems.

(b) Operates at relatively low temperatures.

(c) Can be made with much higher gains, since grid can be wound closer to the cylindrical cathode.

(d) Cathode can be coated with a material which is an efficient electron emitter; such as barium, calcium and strontium oxides.

(4) Indirectly-heated tubes: — Disadvantages.

(a) Longer warm-up time.

(b) Cathode surface is not as rugged as a directly-heated filament.

(c) Cannot be used to supply very high values of current.

Q. 3.50.   Draw a simple circuit diagram consisting of each of the following and describe its operation. Show a signal source and include coupling and by-pass capacitors, power supply connections and plate load.

(a) AF "grounded-cathode" triode amplifier with cathode resistor biasing, as for "Class A" operation.

(b) AF "grounded-cathode" pentode amplifier with battery biasing, for "Class A" operation.

(c) RF "grounded-grid" triode amplifier with LC tank plate-load for "Class B" operation.

(d) AF "cathode-follower" triode amplifier.

(e) AF "push-pull" pentode amplifier operated "Class B" with transformer coupling to a speaker.

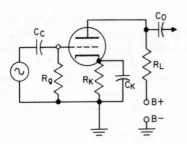

Fig. 3.50(a). Triode-audio amplifier, with cathode bias.

A. (a) See Figure 3.50(a) for diagram of the triode amplifier. The incoming audio frequency signal is applied to the grid through coupling capacitor and C_c, and R_g, the grid resistor. The actual tube-grid signal is developed across R_g which also provides the necessary d–c ground for the grid. The time constant of $R_g \times C_c$ is chosen to pass the lowest desired audio frequency with minimum attenuation. The correct bias for Class A operation is provided by the voltage drop across R_K which occurs because of plate current passing through it. The cathode is thus caused to become positive with respect to the grid (grid is negative with respect to cathode). To prevent degeneration (loss of gain) in the amplifier, R_K is bypassed by a suitable value of capacitor, C_K. The time constant $R_K \times C_K$ is chosen to be at least five times as long as the period of the lowest frequency involved. (The same is true for the time constant of $C_c \times R_g$). The input signal is amplified and inverted in polarity in the plate circuit and appears across the plate load resistor R_L. The output signal is coupled from the amplifier via coupling capacitor, C_o. (See also Q. 3.46b, above.)

(b) See Figure 3.50(b) for diagram of the pentode amplifier. The basic operation of the pentode is the same as the triode (above). However, fixed battery-grid biasing is used. This scheme for biasing is not

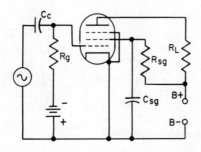

Fig. 3.50(b). Pentode-audio amplifier, with battery bias.

commonly used in Class A audio amplifiers, but has the advantage of being independent of plate and screen grid currents. Fixed bias schemes are seen more frequently in transmitters and for Class AB and Class B audio amplifiers. The correct screen-grid voltage is obtained by the correct value of screen-grid dropping resistor (R_{sg}). Capacitor Csg prevents screen grid degeneration and provides an a–c ground for the shielding effect of the screen. (See also Q. 3.46 (d), above.)

(c) See Q. 3.11 Sup., Supplement No. 1 (Class B operation is achieved by the correct value of fixed bias for the particular tube involved.) Diagram is shown in Fig. 3.50(c), below.

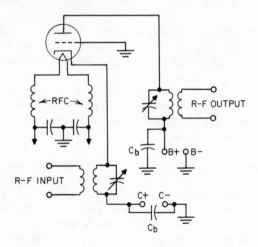

Fig. 3.50(c).   A grounded-grid amplifier.

(d) See Q. 3.18 Sup., Supplement No. 1.

(e) For diagram, see Fig. 3.50(e), below. See Q. 3.436, 3.472, 4.126. Class B operation for an audio amplifier provides maximum efficiency

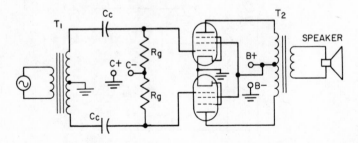

Fig. 3.50(e).   Audio frequency push-pull pentode, Class-B amplifier.

and power output, but this is coupled with higher audio distortion than Class AB or Class A operation in push-pull. Class B single-ended operation cannot ordinarily be used for audio frequencies because of extreme distortion.

Q. 3.51. What kind of vacuum tube responds to filament reactivation and how is reactivation accomplished?

A.   See Q. 3.477.

Q. 3.52. Draw a rough graph of plate-current versus grid-voltage (I_p vs E_g) for various plate voltages on a typical triode vacuum tube.

(a) How would output current vary with input voltage in Class A amplifier operation? Class AB operation? Class B operation? Class C operation?

(b) Does the amplitude of the input signal determine the class of operation?

(c) What is meant by "current-cutoff" bias voltage?

(d) What is meant by plate-current "saturation"?

(e) What is the relationship between distortion in the output current waveform and:

(1) The class of operation?

(2) The portion of the transfer characteristic over which the signal is operating?

(3) Amplitude of input signal?

(f) What occurs in the grid-circuit when the grid is "driven" positive? Would this have any effect on biasing?

(g) In what way is the output current related to the output voltage?

A.   See the illustration. See also Q. 3.122 for bias points of operation.

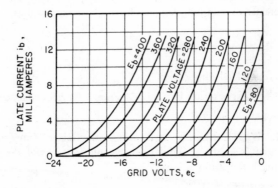

Fig. 3.52. Graph of plate current versus grid voltage for various values of plate voltage for a typical triode. (Transfer characteristics.)

(a)(1) Class A operation: See Q. 3.106, 3.109, 3.133, 3.437.

(2) Class AB operation: With reference to Figure 3.122, the operating point would be between Class A and Class B points. The average plate current will increase with increasing values of grid signal which extend into the Class B region. (For audio amplifiers, two tubes in push-pull must be used to minimize distortion.)

(3) Class B operation: See Q. 3.107, 3.108, 3.443, 3.444, 6.234, 6.425.

(4) Class C operation: See Q. 3.104, 3.137, 3.442, 4.188.

(b) No. The class of operation is determined basically by the grid-bias value. It is possible to overdrive an amplifier, but this does alter its class of operation.

(c) Theoretically, this is the value of bias which will prevent plate current from flowing (no signal input). See also Q. 3.136.

(d) See Q. 3.117.

(e)(1) This has been covered in the above references to this question.

(2) The transfer characteristics are shown in Fig. 3.52. For minimum distortion, operation should not extend into the lower curved portion of the characteristic, for any given plate voltage. Neither should the tube be driven into the region of plate saturation. (See also Q. 3.122).

(3) See (e)(2) above.

(f)(1) Grid current flows in the driven tube. This causes the tube (grid-to-cathode) to present a low impedance to the driving circuit and may cause distortion in audio amplifiers.

(2) If the input circuit was RC coupled, the input coupling capacitor would charge and this would tend to increase the stage bias.

(3) See also Q. 3.278, 3.443, 3.444, and 3.484.

(g) The output current is the current in the tubes' output load, while the output voltage appears across this load. The output current is also the tubes' plate current. This current passing through the load impedance creates the output voltage. This may be expressed as,

$$E_o = I_o \times Z_o,$$
where E_o = output voltage
    I_o = output current
    Z_o = load impedance

Q. 3.53. What is meant by "space charge?" By "secondary emission"?

A. See Q. 3.275, 3.102.

Q. 3.54. What is meant by the "amplification factor" (mu) of a triode vacuum tube (amplifier)? Under what conditions would the amplifier gain approach the value of mu?

A. See Q. 4.182, 4.31.

Q. 3.55. What is meant by "plate resistance" of a vacuum tube? Upon what does its value depend?

A. See Q. 4.182.

Q. 3.56. What is meant by the voltage "gain" of a vacuum tube amplifier? How does it achieve this gain?

A. See Q. 3.113, 3.276.

Q. 3.57. Draw a rough graph of plate-current versus plate supply voltage for three different bias voltages on a typical triode vacuum tube.

(a) Explain, in a general way, how the value of the plate load resistance affects the portion of the curve over which the tube is operating. How is this related to distortion?

(b) Operation over which portion of the curve produces the least distortion?

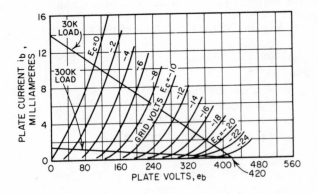

Fig. 3.57. Graph of plate current versus plate supply voltage for a typical triode.

A. (a) As indicated in Figure 3.57 load lines have been drawn in for 30,000 and 300,000 ohm plate-load resistors. Note that the 30,000 ohm load line passes through the grid-bias lines in an area where these are most linear and most evenly spaced. This of course is not true for the 300,000 ohm load line. Changes in grid voltages (input signal) produce corresponding changes in plate currents (output currents) and consequently in plate voltages (output voltages). The least amount of output wave distortion (versus input) will occur when the operation occurs between grid bias lines which are the most evenly spaced and most linear. Therefore, in this example (for least distortion), the 30,000 ohm load would be preferred.

(b) See (a) above.

Q. 3.58. A triode, "grounded cathode," audio amplifier has a mu (amplification factor) of 30, a plate impedance of 5,000 ohms, load impedance of 10,000 ohms, plate voltage of 300 volts, plate current of 10 ma, cathode-resistor bias is used.

(a) What is the stage gain of this amplifier?

(b) What is the cut-off-bias voltage, E_{co}?

(c) Assuming the bias voltage is one-half the value of E_{co}, what value cathode resistor would be used to produce the required bias?

(d) What size capacitor should be used to sufficiently by-pass the cathode resistor if the lowest approximate frequency desired is 500 cycles per second?

A. (a) The stage gain = 20.

(b) The cut-off bias = -10 volts.

(c) The cathode resistor = 500 ohms.

(d) The cathode by-pass capacitor = 3.2 microfarads.

D. (a) Step 1: Find the stage gain of the amplifier,

$$A = \frac{\mu \times R_L}{R_L + R_p} \text{ where}$$

A = gain of the stage.

μ = amplification factor (mu).

R_L = load impedance, in ohms.

R_p = plate impedance of tube in ohms.

$$A = \frac{30 \times 10,000}{10,000 + 5,000} = \frac{300,000}{15,000} = 20$$

(b) Step 2: Find the cut-off bias (E_{co})

$$E_{co} = \frac{E_b}{\mu} \text{ where}$$

E_{co} = grid cut-off bias, in volts.

E_b = plate (supply) voltage, in volts.

μ = amplification factor (mu)

$$E_{co} = \frac{300}{30} = -10 \text{ volts.}$$

(c) Step 3: Find the cathode resistor value for one-half of E_{co}, or -5 volts

$$R_K = \frac{E_K}{I_p} \text{ where}$$

R_K = cathode resistor, in ohms.

E_K = cathode bias, in volts.

I_p = plate current in amperes.

$$R_K = \frac{5}{.01} = 500 \text{ ohms.}$$

(d) Step 4: Find the value of cathode bypass capacitor.

(1) To be effective, the capacitor should have a reactance at least one-fifth or less of the value of the cathode resistor, (or in this case, $X_{CK} = 100$ ohms) at the lowest frequency (or 500 cycles).

(2) $X_{CK} = \dfrac{1}{2\pi \, fC_K}$, or

$$C_K = \frac{1}{2\pi \, fX_{CK}} = \frac{.159}{500 \times 100} = \frac{.159}{50,000} = 3.2 \text{ microfarads.}$$

Q. 3.59. Why is the efficiency of an amplifier operated Class C higher than one operated Class A or Class B?

A. See Q. 3.104, 3.106, 3.107.

Q. 3.60. The following are excerpts from a tube manual rating of a beam pentode. Explain the significance of each item:

(a) Control grid-to-plate capacitance	...	1.1 uuf
(b) Input capacitance	...	2.2 uuf
(c) Output capacitance	...	8.5 uuf
(d) Heater voltage	...	6.3 volts
(e) Maximum dc plate-supply voltage	...	700 volts
(f) Maximum peak positive pulse voltage	...	7,000 volts
(g) Maximum negative pulse plate voltage	...	1,500 volts
(h) Maximum screen grid voltage	...	175 volts
(i) Maximum peak negative control grid voltage	...	200 volts
(j) Maximum plate dissipation	...	20 watts
(k) Maximum screen-grid dissipation	...	30 watts
(l) Maximum dc cathode current	...	200 ma
(m) Maximum peak cathode current	...	700 ma
(n) Maximum control-grid circuit resistance	...	0.47 megohm

A. Examination of an RCA tube manual shows these ratings to be almost identical for type 6CD6-GA television, horizontal-output tube. However, in two instances, the decimal points appear to have been misplaced. Input capacitance should read 22 uuf, instead of 2.2 uuf. Also maximum screen dissipation should read 3.0 watts, not 30 watts. The following is the significance of each listed item:

(a) Control grid to plate capacitance: The measured capacity from the control grid to the plate, with other grids connected to the cathode.

(b) Input capacitance: The sum of control grid-to-cathode, control grid-to-screen grid and control grid-to-suppressor grid (or beam plates) capacitances.

(c) Output capacitance: The sum of plate-to-cathode, plate-to-screen grid and plate-to-suppressor grid (or beam plates) capacitances.

(d) Heater voltage: The nominal cathode heater voltage. It may vary ± 10 percent.

(e) Maximum d–c plate-supply voltage: The maximum steady-state, power-supply voltage permitted to be applied to the plate to restrict the plate dissipation to a safe value.

(f) Maximum positive pulse voltage: In the TV circuit, this occurs during the horizontal flyback time (about 10 μs) when the high-voltage builds up. This (7000 v) is the maximum safe value to prevent internal tube arcing.

(g) Maximum negative pulse voltage: In the TV circuit, this occurs during the horizontal trace (about 53 microseconds and is limited for the same reason as in (f) above.

(h) Maximum screen-grid voltage (d–c): The maximum steady-state, d–c supply voltage permitted to be applied to the screen grid. The screen voltage largely determines plate current (and plate dissipation) as well as screen-grid current and dissipation.

(i) Maximum peak negative control-grid voltage: The maximum safe value to prevent control grid-to-cathode arcing.

(j) Maximum plate dissipation: The maximum safe wattage the plate can dissipate continuously, without causing tube damage (or short life).

(k) Maximum screen-grid dissipation: Same as (j) above, but for screen grid.

(l) Maximum d–c cathode current: The maximum continuous current which the cathode can supply without serious deterioration of the oxide coating of the cathode. The d–c (average) current must be limited to this value.

(m) Maximum peak-cathode current: Within the pulse-width limitations of the TV receiver operation, this is the maximum pulse current the cathode can supply without serious deterioration.

(n) Maximum control-grid circuit resistance: The maximum value of grid to ground resistance. Higher values may result in an excess positive grid voltage caused by positive ion-grid current, which would cancel out the bias and might damage or destroy the tube.

Q. 3.61. Name at least three abnormal conditions which would tend to shorten the life of a vacuum tube, also name one or more probable causes of each condition.

A. 1. (a) Excessive heater voltage.
(b) Excessive plate current.
(c) Inadequate cooling.
(d) Excessive screen-grid current.

(e) Exceeding maximum pulse-current ratings.

2. The causes listed below are keyed to the same letters in 1, above.

(a) Line voltage too high; shorted series-dropping resistor; filament transformer voltage too high.

(b) Bias too low; plate voltage too high; screen grid voltage too high.

(c) Tube shield left off; cooling fan or other cooling scheme not operating.

(d) Bias too low; screen-grid voltage too high.

(e) Pulse-duty cycle too high. In some cases, especially where high voltages are involved, too low a heater voltage may cause cathode damage. In this case, particles of the cathode-oxide coating may be stripped off by the electrostatic field in the tube.

Q. 3.62. Name at least three circuit factors (not including tube types and component values) in a one-stage amplifier circuit, that should be considered at VHF which would not be of particular concern at VLF.

A. The following should be especially considered at VHF:

1. The possibility of circuit oscillation or regeneration due to stray capacitive feedback.

2. The use of low-loss components, such as coil forms, tube sockets, ferrite cores.

3. The use of non-inductive and low-loss by-pass and coupling capacitors, such as ceramic and mica types.

4. Neutralization may be required in some circuits.

5. Use of grounded-grid type of amplifier to reduce feedback problems.

6. Signal lead lengths must be short, to reduce lead inductance.

Q. 3.63. What is a "lighthouse" triode? An "acorn" tube? These tubes were designed for operation in what frequency range?

A. 1. A "lighthouse" triode (or disk-seal tube) is a tube designed especially to operate at UHF. The plate, grid and cathode are assembled in parallel planes instead of coaxially. Extremely close electrode spacing reduces electron transit time. In addition, the electrodes are connected to parallel disks, practically eliminating tube lead inductance. These tubes will amplify up to about 2500 megacycles.

2. Acorn tubes are seldom used in modern electronic equipment. They will amplify up to about 600 megacycles. Acorn tubes are very small (about half the size of a golf ball) and have no base. Electrode connections are brought out to short wire pins which are sealed in a glass rim around the lower portion of the tube.

Q. 3.64. Why are special tubes sometimes required at UHF and above?

A.   Special tubes or tube types are usually required at UHF or higher frequencies. At frequencies above about 100 megacycles, the interelectrode capacitances of ordinary tubes will attenuate the signals greatly. In addition, the ordinary cathode-to-plate, electron-transit time of one-thousandth of a microsecond becomes excessive. At UHF this time approaches or may equal the time of one cycle of the operating frequency, causing undesirable phase shifts within the tube. In addition, the relatively large lead inductance of ordinary tubes limits their operating frequency.

D.   Desirable characteristics of UHF tubes are:

1. Closely spaced electrodes.
2. Small elements.
3. Low-inductance leads.
4. No tube base.

See also Q. 3.63 above.

Q. 3.65.   Draw a diagram of each of the following power supply circuits. Explain the operation of each, including the relative input and output voltage amplitudes, waveshapes, and current waveforms.

(a) Vacuum-tube diode, half-wave rectifier with a capacitive-input "pi-section" filter.

(b) Vacuum-tube diode, full-wave rectifier with choke input (RC) filter.

(c) Silicon diode, doubler-circuit rectifier with a resistive load.

(d) Non-synchronous-vibrator power supply, with silicon diode, bridge-circuit rectifier and capacitive input "pi-section" filter.

(e) Synchronous-vibrator power supply with capacitive input "pi-section" filter.

A.   (a) See Q. 3.488 which shows a two-section pi filter.

(b) For diagram, see Figure 3.65b. For discussion of choke-input

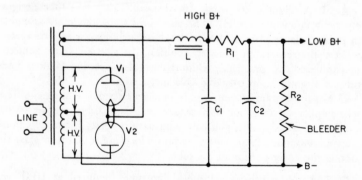

Fig. 3.65(b). Full-wave rectifier with choke-input RC filter.

filter, see Q. 3.401. The resistor in an RC filter is cheaper, smaller and lighter than a choke. However, the d–c drop across the resistor is considerably higher than that across a choke. Therefore, the resistor-type filter can only be used where the large d–c drop can be tolerated (such as in low-level and low-current drain circuits). RC filters are used frequently for power-supply filtering in receivers, tuners and audio amplifiers; as well as in many other types of electronic equipment.

(c) See Q. 4.178. The solid-state diode may be directly substituted for the vacuum tube diodes shown.

(d) *Note:* Although there are many vibrator power supplies in present use, it should be realized that this type of supply is rapidly being replaced by transistor power supplies which have no moving parts and are far more reliable. Refer to Fig. 3.65(d). When power is applied to

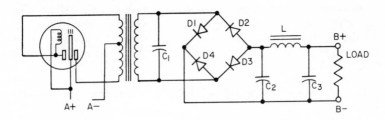

Fig. 3.65(d). Non-synchronous vibrator with bridge rectifier and pi-section filter.

the vibrator coil and transformer primary, the armature is pulled to the left. This shorts out the vibrator coil and the armature springs to the right and touches the right hand contact, after which the magnetic field of the coil and the spring action cause it to touch the left-hand contact. This action becomes cyclical at about 150 to 250 cps. Note that the armature action causes current to flow first in the top half of the primary and then in the bottom half, but in opposite directions. This constitutes an alternating current in the primary which is stepped up in the secondary winding to the desired value. The bridge rectifier shown is a full-wave rectifier and operates as follows:

(1) When the top of the secondary is positive and the bottom negative, electron flow is through the secondary from top to bottom, through D4 to B–, through the load and L, through D2 and back to the top of the transformer.

(2) When the polarities are reversed, electron flow is through D3, up through the secondary, through D1 to B–, through the load and L and back to D3. For filter operation, see Q. 3.488.

(e) See Q. 3.390 and Q. 3.518 (for the diagram). A two-section pi filter is shown. For filter operation, see Q. 3.488.

Q. 3.66. What advantage may a bridge rectifier circuit have over a conventional full-wave rectifier?

A. See Q. 3.65(d), above for diagram of bridge rectifier and (b) of that question for diagram of a full-wave rectifier. The advantages are as follows:

(a) A bridge circuit produces almost double the output voltage, using the same transformer. (Center-tap of secondary is not used.)

(b) For the same output voltage, the inverse-peak voltage is only one-half as much across each tube in a bridge rectifier (4 tubes), compared to a conventional full-wave (2 tubes) rectifier.

D. The same advantage is true when solid-stage rectifiers are used for both (a) and (b) above. Solid-state rectifiers are preferred for bridge circuits for the elimination of the three filament transformers which would be required for vacuum tubes and for their greater reliability and lower internal drop.

Q. 3.67. What are "swinging chokes"? Where are they normally used?

A. See Q. 3.405.

Q. 3.68. Show a method of obtaining two voltages from one power supply.

A. See the figure.

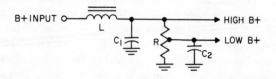

Fig. 3.68. A simple divider method for obtaining two voltages from one power supply.

D. See Q. 4.91 and 6.51.

Q. 3.69. What are the characteristics of a condenser-input filter system as compared to a choke-input system? What is the effect upon a filter choke of a large value of direct current flow?

A. See Q. 3.399, 3.398, 3.401.

Q. 3.70. What is the purpose of a "bleeder" resistor as used in conjunction with power supplies?

A. See Q. 3.182.

Q. 3.71. Would varying the value of the bleeder resistor in a power supply have any effect on the ripple voltage?

A. Generally this would not have any adverse affects. However, if the current rating of the filter choke were exceeded by using too low a value of bleeder, the ripple voltage might be increased.

Q. 3.72. What effect does the amount of current required by the load have upon the voltage regulation of the power supply? Why is voltage regulation an important factor?

A. (1) The greater the amount of current required by the load, the poorer the regulation will tend to be. (Of course a supply can be designed to maintain the required regulation for any practical load).

(2) Regulation is important to maintain virtually constant output supply voltages under varying loads. This prevents inter-modulation of circuits due to power-supply voltage variations as well as possibly insufficient or excessive supply voltages.

D. See Q. 3.403, 3.402, 4.98, 4.100, 6.357.

Q. 3.73. What is meant by the "peak-inverse-voltage" rating of a diode and how can it be computed for a full-wave power supply?

A. See Q. 4.99, 6.351.

Q. 3.74. Discuss the relative merits and limitations as used in power supplies of the following types of rectifiers:
(a) Mercury-vapor diode.
(b) High-vacuum diode.
(c) Copper oxide.
(d) Silicon.
(e) Selenium.

A. (a) Mercury-vapor diode: see Q. 3.178, 3.179, 3.386, 6.335.
(b) High-vacuum diode: see Q. 3.177, 3.179, 6.339, 6.335.
(c) Copper-oxide rectifiers: The merit of this type is that they can (for a given size) supply a relatively large direct current. Limitations of copper-oxide rectifiers are given in Q. 3.189. See also Q. 6.333.
Note: These rectifiers are rapidly being replaced in many uses by germanium and silicon diodes.
(d) Silicon rectifiers: The merits of this type are:
(1) Compact size.

(2) High-current ratings (up to several amperes for larger units).

The major limitation is the relatively low inverse-peak voltage rating of a junction. By stacking units in series, inverse-peak ratings up to several thousand volts can be achieved.

(e) Selenium rectifiers: The merits of this type are:

(1) Higher junction break-down voltage than copper-oxide.

(2) Lower forward resistance than copper oxide and, therefore, greater current-carrying capacity.

(3) Can be used for high-voltage applications by stacking units in series.

(4) Compact in size (for its type).

(5) Low voltage drop across rectifier (about 5 volts). Some limitations of selenium rectifiers are:

(1) Require appreciable space and special mounting facilities.

(2) Must be mounted to obtain adequate cooling.

(3) Appreciably larger size than silicon rectifiers, where they are interchangeable for the same function.

(4) High-shunt capacity, limiting use to power and audio frequencies.

Q. 3.75. Explain the action of a voltage regulator (VR) tube.

A. See Q. 6.337(A) and (B) for schematics of VR tubes. (See also Q. 3.389 for theory of conduction). A VR tube regulates by virtue of the fact that a constant (relatively) voltage drop appears across the tube as long as the tube current remains within the proper limits (usually 5 to 30 ma.). As shown in the figures, the output voltage supply is taken across the tube(s) itself. Variations in either input voltage or output-load current cause varying voltages across the series resistor (R1), but not across the tube itself. The regulation obtained by this means is poorer than when an amplifier-type of regulator is used, but is adequate for many non-critical, low current circuits.

Q. 3.76. If the plate, or plates of a rectifier tube suddenly became red hot, what might be the cause, and how could remedies be effected?

A. See Q. 3.410, 3.409.

Q. 3.77. If a high vacuum type, high voltage rectifier tube suddenly became red hot, what might be the cause, and how could remedies be effected?

A. See Q. 3.409.

Q. 3.78. What does a blue haze in the space between the filament and plate of a high vacuum rectifier tube indicate?

A. See Q. 3.407, 3.98.

INDICATING INSTRUMENTS

Q. 3.79. Make a sketch showing the construction of the D'Arsonval type meter and label the various parts. Draw a circuit diagram of a vacuum-tube-voltmeter and a wattmeter.

A.   (1) For D'Arsonval meter, see Figure 3.79(a). See also Q. 3.184.

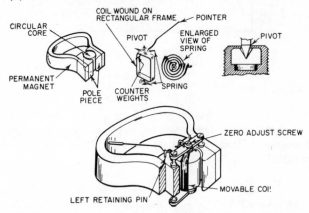

Fig. 3.79(a). Construction details of a D'Arsonval moving-coil mechanism.

(2) For vacuum-tube-voltmeter, see Figure 3.79(b). See also Q. 4.196.

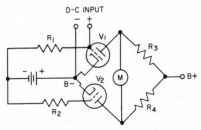

Fig. 3.79(b). Simplified diagram of a balanced triode d–c vacuum-tube-voltmeter.

(3) For wattmeter, see Figure 3.79(c). See also Q. 3.183.

Q. 3.80. Show by a diagram how a voltmeter and ammeter should be connected to measure power in a d.c. circuit.

A.   See Q. 3.303.

Q. 3.81. If a 0–1 d–c milliammeter is to be converted into a voltmeter with a full scale calibration of 100 volts, what value of resistance should be connected in series with the milliammeter.

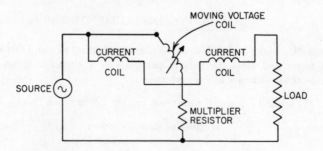

Fig. 3.79(c). Circuit diagram of a wattmeter.

A. See Q. 3.501.

Q. 3.82. A one-milliampere meter having a resistance of 25 ohms was used to measure an unknown current by shunting the meter with a 4 ohm resistor. It then read 0.4 milliampere. What was the unknown current value?

A. See Q. 3.48.

Q. 3.83. An RF VTVM is available to locate resonance of a tunable primary tank circuit of an RF transformer. If the VTVM is measuring the voltage across the tuned secondary, how would resonance of the primary be indicated?

A. Resonance will be indicated by the peak reading of the meter.

D. At resonance the primary tank will offer maximum impedance to the wave and therefore the maximum voltage will be developed across it and coupled to the secondary.

Q. 3.84. Define the following terms and describe a practical situation in which they might be used.
(a) RMS voltage
(b) peak current
(c) average current
(d) power
(e) energy

A. (a) For RMS, see Q. 3.192.
(b) The peak current of any waveform is the greatest instantaneous value of that current. For a sine wave, the peak current equals 1.414 times the RMS value.
Peak currents are important in rectifying devices. The rated peak value should not be exceeded to avoid damage. See also Q. 6.629 through 6.633.

(c) The average current in an a–c circuit is equal to 0.636 of the peak value, or 0.9 of the rms value. (See also Q. 6.630).

The rotation of the moving coil in a d–c meter is proportional to the average value of current flowing in it. However, the scale is generally calibrated in the effective (rms) value, which is the working or heating value of the current.

(d) For definition of electrical power see Q. 3.234. Practical applications are the power used in lamps, heaters and motors (measured in watts.)

(e) For definition of electrical energy, see Q. 3.234. This is measured in watt-hours. A practical application is the watt-hour meter used to measure electrical power consumption.

Q. 3.85.   Describe how horizontal and vertical deflection takes place in a cathode ray oscilloscope. Include a discussion of the wave forms involved.

A.   The usual test oscilloscope has a cathode ray tube utilizing electrostatic deflection plates. (This discussion is keyed to the illustration in Figure 3.85.)

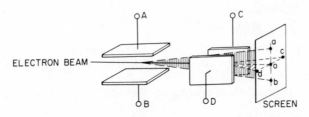

Fig. 3.85. Deflection plates for electrostatic cathode-ray tube.

There are two sets of deflection plates, the vertical deflecting plates (A–B) and the horizontal deflecting plates (C–D). The effect of these deflection plates is based on the fact that an electron beam can be deflected by an electrostatic field. The negative electron beam will be attracted toward the positive plate and repelled from the negative plate. Since the beam is accelerated toward the screen, its electrons are merely shifted in their path and are not ordinarily picked up by the positive deflection plate. If plate A is more positive than plate B, the beam will be deflected upward and will strike the point "a" on the screen. If the potentials are equal (or zero), the beam will strike point "o." Conversely, if plate B is more positive than plate A, the beam will strike at point "b." In the same manner, the beam may be moved horizontally from point "d" to point "c" on the screen.

In practice, a sawtooth deflection voltage is applied to plates C–D. This causes a relatively slow movement of the beam from "d" to "c" and a much more rapid return of the beam from "c" to "d." The rate of this movement is synchronized with the waveform repetition rate of the input waveform to be viewed. This waveform is applied to the vertical deflecting plates, and may be any wave within the limitations of the oscilloscope. The combination of the horizontal (sweep) movement and the vertical signal input causes the input waveform to be traced out on the screen.

OSCILLATORS

Q. 3.86. Draw circuit diagrams of each of the following types of oscillators (include any commonly associated components). Explain the principles of operation of each.
(a) Armstrong
(b) Tuned plate-tuned grid (series fed and shunt fed, crystal and LC-controlled).
(c) Hartley
(d) Colpitts
(e) Electron coupled
(f) Multivibrator
(g) Pierce (crystal controlled)

A. (a) For Armstrong type, see Q. 3.71 and 3.75.
(b)(1) For tuned-plate, tuned-grid, series-fed, LC-controlled type, see Q. 3.69.
(2) For tuned-plate, tuned-grid, shunt-fed, LC-controlled type, see Q. 3.72.
(3) For tuned-plate, tuned-grid, crystal-controlled type, see Q. 3.73 and 3.77.
(c) For Hartley type, see Q. 3.70 and 3.367.
(d) For Colpitts type, see Q. 3.74 and 3.367.
(e) For electron-coupled type, see Q. 3.76.
(f) For multivibrator type, see Q. 4.104 for diagram and Q. 3.429 for discussion.
(g) For Pierce type, see Q. 6.413.

Q. 3.87. What are the principal advantages of crystal control over tuned-circuit oscillators?

A. See Q. 3.423.

Q. 3.88. Why should excessive feedback be avoided in a crystal oscillator?

A. See Q. 3.420.

Q. 3.89. Why is a separate source of plate power desirable for a crystal oscillator stage in a radio transmitter?

A. See Q. 3.422.

Q. 3.90. What may result if a high degree of coupling exists between the plate and grid circuits of a crystal controlled oscillator?

A. See Q. 3.420.

Q. 3.91. Explain some methods of determining if oscillation is occurring in an oscillator circuit.

A. See Q. 6.526.

Q. 3.92. What is meant by parasitic oscillations; how may they be detected and prevented?

A. See Q. 3.372. They may be detected by tuning for them with a wavemeter or heterodyne frequency meter. For a more detailed discussion, see Q. 3.126 of this supplement.

Q. 3.93. What determines the fundamental frequency of a quartz crystal?

A. The fundamental frequency of a quartz crystal is dependent upon the following factors:
1. The crystal's physical dimensions.
2. Capacitance of the crystal holder.
3. The orientation of the slab cut from the natural crystal.
4. The crystal substance.

D. See Q. 3.419, 3.416, 3.248.

Q. 3.94. What is meant by the temperature coefficient of a crystal?

A. See Q. 3.417, 3.414 and 3.418.

Q. 3.95. What are the characteristics and possible uses of an "overtone" crystal? A "third mode" crystal?

A. 1. An "overtone" crystal is one specially ground to oscillate at an odd harmonic of its fundamental frequency. Crystals are available to oscillate at frequencies up to 100 mc. Most standard crystals will oscillate on their third and fifth overtones using suitable circuitry. Overtone crystals are commonly used for oscillators in vhf transmitters. (Often in conjunction with frequency-multiplier stages.)
2. A "third mode" crystal is one which is operated on the third harmonic of its fundamental frequency.

Q. 3.96. Explain some of the factors involved in the stability of an oscillator (both crystal and LC-controlled).

A. Some of the important factors are:
1. C to L ratio of tank circuit. (See Q. 3.297).
2. A stable and separate power supply. See Q. 3.89 above.
3. Components with very low temperature coefficients.
4. Low loss components, including tank circuit elements, by-pass capacitors and tube sockets.
5. Constant temperature operation, such as enclosing critical circuits in a temperature-controlled oven.
6. Use of high-Q, frequency determining elements, including the important factor of stable-crystal control.
7. Isolation of the oscillator from its load. (See Q. 3.298).
8. The use of temperature compensating components, such as capacitors with a negative-temperature coefficient.

Q. 3.97. Is it necessary or desirable that the surfaces of a quartz crystal be clean? If so, what cleaning agents may be used which will not adversely affect the operation of the crystal?

A. See Q. 3.425.

Q. 3.98. What is the purpose of a buffer amplifier stage in a transmitter?

A. See Q. 3.298.

AUDIO AMPLIFIERS

Q. 3.99. Draw simple schematic diagrams illustrating the following types of coupling between audio amplifier stages and between a stage and a load.
(a) Triode vacuum tube inductively coupled to a loudspeaker.
(b) Resistance coupling between two pentode vacuum tubes.
(c) Impedance coupling between two tetrode vacuum tubes.
(d) A method of coupling a high impedance loudspeaker to an audio-frequency amplifier tube without flow of plate current through the speaker windings, and without the use of a transformer.

A. (a) For inductive coupling, see Q. 3.79.

(b) For resistance coupling, see Q. 3.80, which shows two triodes. With pentodes, the coupling is identical.

(c) For impedance coupling, see Q. 3.82. For tetrodes, the coupling is identical (practically obsolete method).

(d) For high-impedance speaker coupling, see Q. 3.78 (practically obsolete method.)

Q. 3.100.   What would probably be the effect on the output amplitude and waveform if the cathode-resistor by-pass capacitor in an audio stage were removed?

A.   The output amplitude would be reduced and the output waveform might be improved.

D.   See Q. 3.438 and Q. 4.33.

Q. 3.101.   Why do vacuum tubes produce random noise?

A.   Vacuum tube random noise (or shot-effect noise) is caused by random irregularities in the flow of electrons within the tube.

D.   Shot-effect is caused by the fact that electrons are discreet particles which are emitted from the cathode in a random manner, rather than as a smooth continuous "fluid-like" flow. The current resulting from such an emission causes variations in the output circuit, commonly called "noise." The "noise" energy is distributed evenly across the entire frequency spectrum.

Q. 3.102.   Why are de-coupling resistors and capacitors used in stages having a common power supply?

A.   See Q. 6.261.

Q. 3.103.   How would saturation of an output transformer create distortion?

A.   When saturation of an output transformer has been reached, the inductance value is greatly reduced. This causes two immediate effects:

(a) A reduction of load impedance on the output tube which reduces output amplitudes, especially at the low frequencies and thus creates amplitude distortion.

(b) The inability of a saturated transformer to pass the waveform through to the speaker, without severe change. This happens because the flux in the transformer is already at its (practical) maximum value and cannot increase to follow the waveform pattern. This causes severe audio distortion.

Q. 3.104.   Why is noise often produced when an audio signal is distorted?

A.   Whether or not "noise" is actually present when an audio signal is distorted depends largely upon the actual cause of the distortion. Simple amplitude or frequency distortion will not necessarily produce any

noise. Some cases where noise may accompany audio distortion may result from:
1. Defective coupling capacitor.
2. Microphonic tube.
3. Microphonic connections or components.
4. Defective volume control.

D. While the usual concept of audible "noise" is not involved here, both harmonic and intermodulation distortion frequencies will appear in a distorted audio signal. These components may seem to add noise to the output signal.

Q. 3.105. What are the factors which determine the correct bias voltage for the grid of a vacuum tube?

A. See Q. 3.136.

Q. 3.106. Draw schematic diagrams illustrating the following types of grid biasing and explain their operation.
(a) Battery
(b) Power supply
(c) Voltage divider
(d) Cathode-resistor

A. (a) For battery bias, see Q. 3.50(b), above.
(b) For power supply bias, see Fig. 3.106(b) and Q. 3.50(c) and (e),

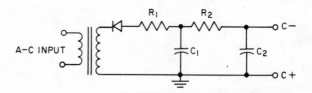

Fig. 3.106(b). A simple power supply to provide vacuum-tube bias.

above, for diagrams. In this scheme the desired value of bias is provided by means of a separate power supply. The current provided by such a supply is negligible, so that small solid-state rectifiers and simple RC filters may be employed in a half-wave rectifier.

(c) For a diagram of a voltage-divider bias scheme see Figure 3.106 (c). In this bias scheme, the center-tap of the high-voltage secondary is returned to ground only through the low end of the bleeder resistor. This provides a negative d-c voltage with respect to ground, whose amplitude is proportional to the percentage of the bleeder resistance tapped to ground.

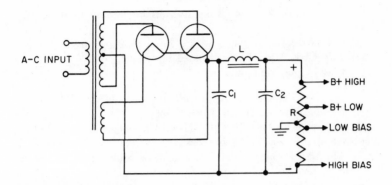

Fig. 3.106(c). Schematic showing how to obtain voltage-divider bias.

(d) For cathode bias, see Q. 3.50(a), above. Also see Q. 3.284.

Q. 3.107. Is grid-leak biasing practical in audio amplifier stages?

A. Grid-leak biasing is not practical in audio amplifier stages.

D.   The value of grid-leak bias is proportional to the amplitude of the input-grid signal. This type of bias varies whenever the signal changes and thus the operating point of the tube also changes. This condition may cause severe distortion of the audio signal. In addition, the grid current required to produce grid-leak bias causes loading on the driver stage reducing its gain and causing additional waveform distortion. For a discussion of grid-leak bias, see Q. 3.368.

Q. 3.108.   Draw a diagram showing a method of obtaining grid bias for a filament type vacuum tube by use of resistance in the plate circuit of the tube.

A.   See Q. 3.285.

Q. 3.109.   Explain how you would determine the approximate value of cathode bias resistance necessary to provide correct grid bias for any particular amplifier.

A.   See Q. 3.143.

Q. 3.110.   Draw circuit diagrams and explain the operation (including input-output phase relationships, approximate practical voltage gain, approximate stage efficiency, uses, advantages, and limitations) of each of the following types of audio circuits.
  (a) Class A amplifier with cathode-resistor biasing.
  (b) Cathode-follower amplifier.

(c) **At least two types of phase inverters for feeding push-pull amplifiers.**

(d) **Cascaded Class A stages with a form of current feedback.**

(e) **Two Class A amplifiers operated in parallel.**

(f) **Class A push-pull amplifier.**

A.   (a) Class A amplifier, with cathode-resistor biasing:

(1) For diagram, see Figure 3.50(a), above.

(2) For operation, see Q. 3.50, above. The output wave is 180 degrees out of phase with the input wave.

(3) The actual voltage gain which may be achieved depends upon the tube in use and the circuitry. An example of finding the voltage gain of a stage is given in Q. 3.58, above. (See also Q. 4.182, 4.31, 3.113, 3.276.)

(4) The approximate stage efficiency is 25 percent. (See Q. 3.106).

(5) This type of amplifier may be used as an audio pre-amplifier, audio-intermediate amplifier, or final audio amplifier. It may also be used as a receiver r–f amplifier or i–f amplifier. It also has many uses in various stages of different types of test equipment.

(6) Advantages and limitations are described in Q. 3.106.

(b) Cathode-follower stage:

(1) For diagram, See Fig. 3.18, Sup., (Supplement No. 1).

(2) For operation, see Q. 3.18, Sup., (Supplement No. 1). In the cathode follower, the output (taken from the cathode) is always in phase with the grid-input signal.

(3) The voltage gain is always less than one and depends upon the tube and circuitry in use. For the method of calculating gain, see Q. 3.18, Sup., (Supplement No. 1).

(4) Plate circuit efficiency is not a factor in a cathode follower since the output is taken across the cathode circuit. However, for a Class A-biased stage, the efficiency is comparable to a Class A-biased conventional amplifier, or about 25 percent.

(5) A cathode follower is most often used to drive a low-impedance device from a high-impedance input. It is frequently used to feed a low-impedance transmission line from a high impedance source and is commonly used for this purpose in connection with pulse circuits. Because of its low-impedance output, its output is affected relatively little by the affects of shunt capacities of the load. It is sometimes used to feed a loudspeaker voice coil directly and thus eliminate the need for an output transformer. However, relatively high impedance voice coils are required (25-50 ohms) in this case.

(6) The advantage of the cathode follower lies in the fact that it is a simple but highly effective impedance reducer. It also has a very wide frequency response and passes narrow pulses without appreciable dis-

tortion. Its only serious limitation is the fact that its voltage gain is always less than one.

(c) Two types of phase inverters: These are covered one at a time, the first one discussed is the single tube (paraphase) amplifier.

(1) For diagram, see Figure 3.19 Sup., (Supplement No. 1).

(2) As shown in the figure, one output is taken from the plate (inverted) and one from the cathode (not inverted). In practice, R_K is made equal to R_L and equal outputs are thus obtained since the same current flows through both resistors.

(3) The voltage gain of each output is always less than one because of the negative feedback across R_K.

(4) Plate circuit efficiency is about 25 percent.

(5) The paraphase amplifier is used to drive a push-pull amplifier from a single-ended input.

(6) The advantage of this circuit is that it requires only a single tube, and has excellent frequency response. Its limitation is that it has no voltage gain.

Note: The second type of phase inverter to be discussed below is called a cathode-coupled paraphase amplifier.

(1) For diagram, see Figure 3.110(c).

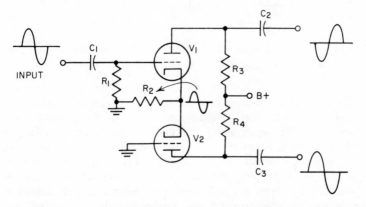

Fig. 3.110(c). Schematic of a cathode-coupled paraphase inverter.

(2) Observe in the figure that the common cathode resistor R_2 is unbypassed and that the grid of V_2 is grounded. R_2 is chosen so that the signal across it is equal to one-half of the V_1 grid-input signal. The effective signals applied to both tubes are equal since the R_2 signal is degenerative for V_1, but not for V_2. The output of V_1 is inverted with respect to the input signal. However, the output of V_2 is not because its input signal is applied to its cathode and not to the grid.

(3) The voltage gain of each stage is equal to one-half of its normal gain because of the cathode signal action. For gain-calculation references, see part (a)(3) of this question.

(4) The approximate plate efficiency of each tube is 25 percent.

(5) The use of this amplifier is the same as for the paraphase amplifier discussed above.

(6) This circuit has the advantage of providing voltage gain at each plate and good frequency response. However, the frequency response is poorer than in the prior phase inverter and it has only one-half the gain provided by conventional amplifier circuits.

(d) Cascaded Class-A stages with current feedback.

(1) For diagram of cascaded Class-A stages, see Fig. 3.110(d).

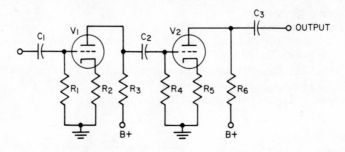

Fig. 3.110(d). Simplified schematic of a two-stage audio amplifier employing current feedback in both stages.

(2) In practice, voltage feedback over two stages is generally preferred, or a combination of voltage and current feedback may be found quite often. The circuit of Fig. 3.110(d) employs current feedback in both stages by virtue of the unbypassed cathode resistors. The polarity of signal at each cathode is the same as that appearing at its corresponding grid. Therefore degeneration (negative feedback) occurs in each stage. This is current feedback because the voltage at each cathode depends upon the plate current of each tube flowing through the individual cathode resistors (R_2 and R_5).

(3) The voltage gain of each stage is modified (reduced) by the negative feedback and may be found from the equation

$$A' = \frac{\mu R_L}{(\mu + 1) R_K + r_p + R_L} \text{ where}$$

A' = Gain with feedback.

μ = Amplification factor.

R_L = Plate-load resistance.

R_K = Cathode resistance.

r_p = Plate resistance (internal).

(4) The approximate plate efficiency of each stage is 25 percent.

(5) This type of amplifier may be used as intermediate audio-amplifier stages in various types of audio systems, or as intermediate amplifier stages in an oscilloscope, or other test equipment.

(6) Advantages of this type of amplifier include; reduced distortion, improved frequency response, improved stability from regeneration or oscillation, reduction of hum and noise. The only serious limitation is the reduced gain.

(e) Two Class-A amplifiers operated in parallel.

(1) For diagram, see Figure 3.110(e).

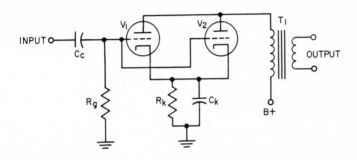

Fig. 3.110(e). Schematic diagram of two Class-A amplifiers in parallel.

(2) Operation is basically the same as for a single tube as discussed in part (a) of this question. However, in this case, the proper cathode bias depends upon the plate current of both tubes. Two tubes in parallel provide double the power output of one tube. Distortion remains the same as for one tube and the grid input voltage remains the same. The effective internal-plate resistance is half that of one tube and thus the required plate load impedance is cut in half.

(3) The voltage gain is unchanged by the use of two tubes in parallel. However, this factor is seldom important since power output is the reason for paralleling the two tubes.

(4) The approximate plate efficiency of each tube is 25 percent.

(5) This type of amplifier, while not popular, may be used as an audio power-output amplifier. In general the push-pull type is preferred.

(6) The principal advantage of this configuration is the elimination of the phase splitter required for push-pull operation. Limitations include; double the d–c plate current requiring a special and expensive output transformer, no reduction in distortion as with push-pull opera-

tion and the larger cathode by-pass capacitor required because of the half value of the cathode-bias resistor. (See Q. 3.438).

(f) Class-A push-pull amplifier.

(1) For diagram, see Figure 3.110(f).

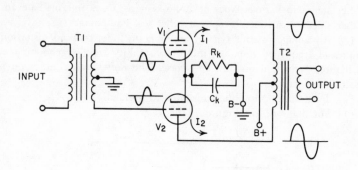

Fig. 3.110(f). Schematic diagram of a Class-A push-pull amplifier.

(2) The proper inputs could be supplied from a phase inverter (see part (c) of this question), but is here provided by a center-tapped input transformer. The two grids are fed with signals which are 180 degrees out of phase. As a result, the plate signal currents (I_1 and I_2) are also 180 degrees out of phase. However, these currents flow in opposite directions through the primary winding and so are additive in the secondary winding.

(3) Voltage gain is not a consideration here, but the power output is twice that for an amplifier using one of the same output tubes. (See also Q. 6.253).

(4) The approximate plate efficiency of each tube is 25 percent.

(5) The most common use of this amplifier is as the audio power-output stage feeding a loudspeaker.

(6) For advantages, see Q. 3.436. Limitations include; the need to supply out-of-phase grid signals, and matched tubes and transformer windings for best results. Bias controls may be required to assure perfect balancing.

Q. 3.111. Why does a Class-B audio frequency amplifier stage require considerably greater driving power than a Class-A amplifier?

A. See Q. 3.443 and 3.444.

Q. 3.112. Show by use of circuit diagrams two ways of using single-ended stages to drive a push-pull output stage.

A. (1) A paraphase amplifier is one method and is shown in Figure 3.19 Sup., (Supplement No. 1). This is discussed in Q. 3.110(c) Sup. No. 3.

(2) A second type of phase inverter is shown in Figure 3.112. The voltage divider has a ratio equal to the voltage gain of V_1.

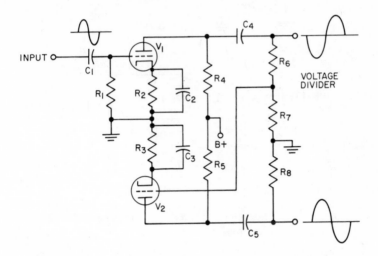

Fig. 3.112. Single-ended stages arranged to drive a push-pull output stage.

Q. 3.113. Draw circuit diagrams and explain the operation of two commonly used tone control circuits and explain their operation.

A. See Figures 3.113(a) and 3.113(b).

(a) In the circuit of Figure 3.113(a) the tone-control elements are C_T and R_T. This is a very simple, but popular, circuit and provides high-frequency attenuation only. When the slider of R_T is at the top, C_T is fully effective in bypassing the higher audio frequencies. When R_T is at the bottom end (maximum series resistance), the effect of C_T is nullified and all high audio frequencies are passed to the grid of the tube.

(b) The circuit of Figure 3.113(b) is more complex and provides both bass and treble attenuation. When C_1 goes to the grid side of R_2, low frequencies are attenuated by the effect of the series reactance of C_1, but this effect is limited by the bypass effect of R_1. When C_1 is at the ground end of R_2 high frequencies are attenuated by the bypass effect to ground of C_1.

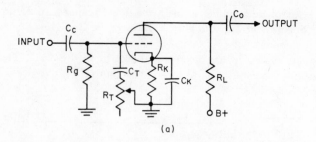

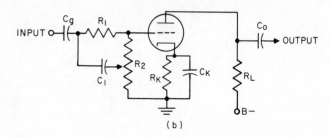

Fig. 3.113(a) and (b). Schematics of two commonly used tone-control circuits.

Q. 3.114. Name some causes of hum and self-oscillation in audio amplifiers and the methods of reducing it.

A. (a) Hum may be caused by:

(1) Heater-to-cathode tube leakage. The tube must be replaced to cure this.

(2) Filament-wire radiation. (See Q. 3.511 for discussion.)

(3) Open-grid circuit. The high-impedance grid is susceptible to hum-radiation pickup. The cure is obvious.

(4) Faulty filter capacitor (or resistor or choke) in the power supply filter feeding the amplifier. Again, the cure is obvious.

(5) Hum pickup from a power transformer due to its inadequate shielding or its close proximity to a high gain stage. This may be corrected by replacing the transformer or by proper shielding of the tube(s) involved and their input (grid) leads. Proper dress of the input leads may also be effective in reducing hum pickup.

(b) For self-oscillation, see Q. 3.510, 6.261, 3.465.

Q. 3.115. What factors should be taken into consideration when ordering a Class-A audio-output transformer; a Class-B audio-output transformer feeding a speaker of known ohmic value?

A. (a) Some important considerations when ordering a Class-A, audio-output transformer are:

(1) Operating power level in watts, including peak-power level expected.

(2) Turns ratio to match speaker voice coil to the output tube(s).

(3) Single ended or push-pull power output stage.

(4) Frequency response under normal power-output conditions.

(5) Harmonic distortion at the lowest frequency involved and at the maximum-output power.

(6) Direct current in primary winding(s).

(7) Adequate magnetic and electrostatic shielding.

(8) Source impedance and load impedance.

(b) Important considerations for a Class-B output transformer are the same as for Class-A (above) with one added consideration. Since the plate currents flow intermittently (180 degrees) in each tube, it is essential that the leakage inductance between both halves of the primary windings be very small. If this is not true, transients will be produced in the primaries, that may produce severe distortion.

Q. 3.116. Draw a diagram of a single-button carbon microphone circuit, including the microphone transformer and source of power.

A. See Q. 3.95.

Q. 3.117. If low impedance head telephones of the order of 75 ohms are to be connected to the output of a vacuum tube amplifier, how may this be done to permit most satisfactory operation?

A. This may be done by using a suitable audio transformer. The transformer should have adequate frequency response and the correct turns ratio to match the 75 ohm phones to the output tube impedance.

D. See Q. 3.40 above.

Q. 3.118. Describe the construction and explain the operation of a "crystal" type microphone; a "carbon button" microphone.

A. 1. For crystal microphone, see Q. 3.337 and 6.236.

2. For carbon microphone, see Q. 3.338.

Q. 3.119. What precaution should be observed when using and storing crystal microphones?

A. The microphone should be protected against excessive heat, shock and humidity.

D. See Q. 3.337.

RADIO FREQUENCY AMPLIFIERS

Q. 3.120.   What is an RFC? Why are they used?

A.   See Q. 3.357.

Q. 3.121.   What are the advantages of using a resistor in series with the cathode of a Class-C radio-frequency amplifier tube to provide bias?

A. If the exciting signal to a Class-C radio-frequency amplifier, using grid-leak bias only, is interrupted for any reason the bias will be reduced to zero and excessive d-c plate current will flow; usually with disastrous results. If at least a portion of the total bias is obtained from a resistor in series with the cathode, the bias will not be reduced to zero because the d-c plate current, flowing through the cathode resistor, will still provide some bias.

D.   This remaining bias can be made just sufficient to allow no more than the maximum allowable plate dissipation to occur under the d-c conditions of no excitation. For example, consider a type 833-A triode being used as a Class-C rf amplifier with a plate voltage of 2500 volts. The maximum allowable plate dissipation for this tube is 300 watts. Under no-excitation conditions, all of the plate power input is converted to plate dissipation which, in this case, will reach the maximum allowable when the d-c plate current is 120 milliamperes. Reference to the characteristic curves for the tube will indicate that approximately −40 volts grid bias will produce a d-c plate current of 120 ma. Using Ohm's Law, the value of resistance to be used is found to be 40/0.120 or 333 ohms.

If the total grid bias recommended is −300 volts, the remaining 260 volts can be obtained in the usual manner by means of a grid leak.

Q. 3.122.   What is the difference between RF voltage amplifiers and RF power amplifiers in regards to applied bias? What type of tube is generally employed in RF voltage amplifiers?

A.   Normally, an RF voltage amplifier is operated as a Class-A amplifier, whereas an RF power amplifier is operated as either a Class-B or Class-C amplifier. Therefore, an RF voltage amplifier would normally use a bias that is approximately midway between zero and the cut-off bias for the value of plate voltage employed. For a Class-B power amplifier the bias would be approximately equal to the cut-off bias and for a Class-C power amplifier the bias would be in the order of twice cut-off bias. See also Question 3.122 and its accompanying diagram.

Since power amplification is not required of RF voltage amplifiers, receiving type tubes are normally used for this function. Commonly, these are pentodes, although triodes are sometimes used under special circumstances.

Q. 3.123. Draw schematic diagrams of the following circuits and give some possible reasons for their use.

(a) Link coupling between a final RF stage and an antenna. (Include a low pass filter.)

(b) Capacitive coupling between an oscillator stage and a buffer amplifier.

(c) A method of coupling a final stage to a quarter-wave Marconi antenna other than link or transmission line.

A.   (a) Link coupling between a final RF stage and an antenna is most useful when the antenna is located remotely from the transmitter building as is the case in most broadcast stations. This permits placing both the building and the antenna in the most advantageous physical locations. Figure 3.123(a), illustrates the pertinent details of the system.

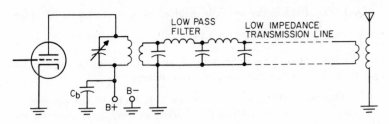

Fig. 3.123(a). *Link coupling between a final r–f stage and an antenna.*

(b) Capacitive coupling between an oscillator and its buffer amplifier is a very simple and easily adjustable method. For greater coupling, the tap on the tank coil of the oscillator may be moved closer to the plate end of the coil. Figure 3.123(b), illustrates the basic scheme for this type of coupling. See also Q. 3.298.

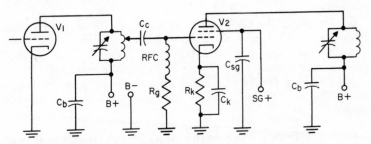

Fig. 3.123(b). *Capacitive coupling between an oscillator stage and a buffer amplifier.*

(c) For shipboard installations where the intermediate frequency ranges are used, the antenna's physical size is such that the connections to it from the transmitter necessarily are part of the complete antenna system. In such circumstances, the antenna downlead, which is a portion of the antenna itself, is connected directly to the transmitter output terminals. The diagrams shown for Question 3.83 (A and B) illustrate two methods for accomplishing this. It should be noted that all parts shown in the diagrams are included inside the transmitter enclosure and just the antenna and ground connections are made to the transmitter.

Q. 3.124. Draw a schematic diagram of a grounded-grid RF amplifier and explain its operation.

A. See Question 4.189 for the diagram of a grounded-grid RF amplifier. See Q. 4.185 and Q. 3.11 Sup., (Supplement No. 1) for discussion.

Q. 3.125. Explain the principle involved in neutralizing an RF stage.

A. See Questions 3.307 and 3.441.

Q. 3.126. State some indications of, and methods of testing for, the presence of parasitic oscillations in a transmitter.

A. Question 3.370 gives some of the indications of the presence of parasitic oscillations in a transmitter. Some methods of testing for the existence of such parasitics are as follows:

(a) Using a radio receiver or sensitive wavemeter to explore the frequency spectra on either side of the desired operating frequency during both modulated and unmodulated conditions. Parasitic oscillations will show up as extra frequencies produced in addition to the desired operating frequency.

(b) Observing the modulation envelope, preferably using a trapezoidal pattern, with an oscilloscope with and without constant tone modulation. The presence of parasitics will cause unexplained nonlinearities, the degree of which will vary with differing percentages of modulation.

(c) Measuring the efficiency of the amplifier tube at the operating frequency. If the tube is operating with rated dissipation and power input, but the output at the operating efficiency is too low, the "missing" power output represents power output at a parasitic frequency.

(d) Checking for the overheating of one or more amplifier components. The radio frequency chokes and bypass capacitors are especially suspect.

Q. 3.127. Draw a circuit diagram of a push-pull (triode) final power amplifier with transmission line feed to a shunt fed quarter wave antenna and indicate a method of plate neutralization.

A.   See the figure.

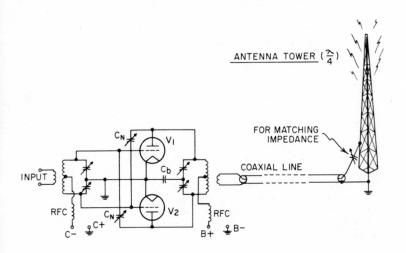

Fig. 3.127. Neutralized push-pull final amplifier; transmission-line
fed to a shunt-fed quarter-wave antenna.

D.   See Q. 3.307 for neutralization discussion.

Q. 3.128.   Explain, step-by-step, at least one procedure for neutral-izing an RF amplifier stage.

A.   See Question 3.441.

Q. 3.129.   Draw a circuit diagram of a push-push frequency multi-plier and explain its principle of operation.

A.   For the diagram see the figure. For the principle of operation see Questions 4.84, 3.138 and 3.139.

Q. 3.130.   Push-pull frequency multipliers normally produce what order of harmonics; even or odd?

A.   Since the push-pull amplifier has been especially designed to re-duce or eliminate all even-order harmonics, it follows that such an am-plifier when used as a frequency multiplier will operate successfully only on odd-order harmonics. See also Q. 3.129, above.

Q. 3.131.   Draw a schematic diagram and explain the operation of a harmonic generator stage.

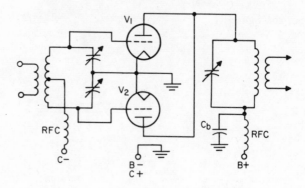

Fig. 3.129. A push-push frequency multiplier.

A. For the diagram see Question 3.90. For the principle of operation see Question 3.138. See also Q. 3.129 and 3.130 above.

Q. 3.132. What class of amplifier is appropriate to use in a radio frequency doubler stage?

A. Class C amplifier.

D. See Q. 3.129, 3.130 and 3.131, above.

Q. 3.133. Describe some factors in connection with the following items, which should be considered at VHF and above but would not be of particular concern at MF or below.
(a) Wire diameter and length.
(b) Wiring configuration (placement and bending).
(c) Coaxial cables and transission lines.
(d) Capacitor types.

A. (a) To minimize the self-inductance of wires carrying VHF currents it is necessary to use conductors that are as short as possible and with as large a diameter as feasible. The diameter, however, should not be increased to the extent of appreciably increasing the capacitance of such conductors to ground or other conductors.

(b) Wiring configuration should be such that each conductor is separated by as great a distance from other conductors and ground as possible to minimize any distributed capacitances.

Any bends in the conductors should be minimum in number and of a maximum in radius as possible within the physical confines of the space available. This is to minimize the self-inductance of such conductors.

(c) The insulation of coaxial cables and transmission lines should be of a material having the lowest possible dielectric losses. Certain materials exhibit negligible losses at MF but have substantial losses at VHF. Insofar as is possible, such cables and lines should be air insulated. Where physical support is required, the number of such supports should be as few as possible. If standing waves are normally present on such cables and lines, it is important that insulating supports only be located at points of minimum voltage.

(d) Variable capacitors used in VHF service should be air insulated, using a minimum of solid dielectric for supporting the capacitor plates. Such dielectric that is used should have as small a dielectric loss as possible. Fixed capacitors should have low loss dielectrics, such as mica or ceramic.

TRANSMITTERS

Q. 3.134. Discuss the following items with respect to their harmonic attenuating properties as possibly used in a transmitter or receiver.
  (a) Link coupling
  (b) Tuned circuits
  (c) Degree of coupling
  (d) Bias voltage
  (e) Decoupling circuits
  (f) Shielding

A. (a) Link coupling has, to a small degree, some attenuating properties for harmonics due to the relatively high capacitance of the low impedance transmission line connecting the two coupling coils. The capacitance will offer decreasing reactance as the frequencies increase and thus tend to by-pass harmonics to a greater extent than the fundamental frequency.

(b) Tuned circuits, resonant to the fundamental frequency, discriminate against harmonic frequencies to a remarkable degree. This discrimination, and hence harmonic attenuation, is a function of the Q of the tuned circuits and it is therefore desirable to have as high a Q as practical, if harmonic reduction is a prime consideration.

(c) In coupled-tuned circuits it is best to use loose coupling to achieve harmonic attenuation. The effect of such loose coupling is to "sharpen" the frequency response curve of the coupled circuits and, in a sense, increase the operating Q's of each of the tuned circuits.

(d) Bias voltage in Class-A, Class-B and Class-B Linear RF amplifiers is extremely important from the standpoint of the reduction of harmonic generation. If the bias is incorrect in these amplifiers, a distorted output is obtained and harmonics of the input signal therefore appear. It should be noted, however, that already existing harmonics in the input signal will appear in the output undiminished and therefore the correct bias will not aid in the attenuation of such harmonics. Any harmonic attenuation in these amplifiers will be due to the action of the tuned circuits only.

(e) Since decoupling circuits are employed to reduce or eliminate positive feedback in multi-stage amplifiers, distortion in such amplifiers is reduced and, therefore, the generation of harmonics is reduced. However, if harmonics are present in the input signal, harmonics will appear in the output to the same degree despite the use of decoupling circuits. If the amplifiers are tuned, any harmonic attenuation will be due to the tuned circuits only.

(f) Shielding, when properly used, can be very effective in harmonic attenuation; especially when used as electrostatic or Faraday shields between coupled tuned circuits. Used in this manner, the shields drastically reduce the capacitive coupling between such circuits and thus reduce the transfer of harmonic energy from one circuit to the other. See Questions 3.373, 3.371 and 4.62 for diagram.

Q. 3.135. Define "transmitter intermodulation," a possible cause (or causes), its effects and steps that could be taken to reduce it.

A. Transmitter intermodulation is the generation, by a transmitter, of a frequency, or frequencies, which is the combination of the fundamental or any of its harmonics with another fundamental or harmonics from a second transmitter which is fairly close by. One common cause of this is the picking up, by the antenna, some of the radiated energy from the second transmitter which is then fed backward into the transmitter over the transmission line. A portion of this energy can then be transferred to the grid of the power amplifier. Since at least the grid of this amplifier is a non-linear circuit, a modulation of one frequency, or its harmonics, by the second frequency, or its harmonics, takes place with resulting sideband frequencies. These sideband frequencies are known as intermodulation products and may be equal to $f_1 \pm f_2$, $f_1 \pm 2f_2$, $2f_1 \pm f_2$, etc.

One obvious manner of reducing such intermodulation would be to locate the transmitters and their associated antennas at greater distances from one another. Economic and other reasons, however, often eliminate this remedy. By placing a wavetrap, tuned to the second transmitter's frequency or offending harmonic, in the transmission line close to the transmitter, the picked up energy can be markedly reduced, with a corresponding reduction in the intermodulation. RF-power amplifiers using inductive neutralization are prone to these intermodulation effects because the neutralization is only effective for the operating frequency and energy transfer from output to input at frequencies appreciably different from the operating frequency takes place quite easily. Plate or grid neutralization, on the other hand, is effective over quite a large frequency spectrum and such energy transfer is more effectively blocked.

Q. 3.136. State a probable cause of and method of reducing transmitter spurious emissions (other than harmonics).

A. Parasitic oscillations and emissions are an important form of spurious radiation. For a discussion of their generation and elimination see Question 3.372.

Q. 3.137. List several frequently used methods of attenuating harmonics in transmitters and explain how each works.

A. Several frequently used methods of attenuating harmonics in transmitters are as follows:

(a) The use of a Farady screen between the final tank inductance and the output coupling coil of the transmitter. For a discussion of this method, see Question 3.373, and 4.62.

(b) The use of tuned wave traps in the transmission line to the antenna. The diagram shown for Question 4.62 shows how such traps may be connected in the transmission line. The parallel resonant traps shown connected in series with the line present a very high impedance to the harmonic frequency to which they are tuned and therefore reduce the amount of harmonic energy transferred to the antenna. The series resonant traps shown connected from the line to ground exhibit a very low impedance to the harmonic frequency and tend to short circuit the harmonic energy to ground, thus reducing the amount of such energy from reaching the antenna.

(c) Low pass RF filters are sometimes used in the transmission line instead of the tuned filters discussed above. The low pass filters are designed to have a cut-off frequency somewhat in excess of the operating frequency. These filters not only reduce the harmonic radiation but have the added advantage of attenuating any other spurious emissions above the filter's cut-off frequency. See Q. 3.35, 3.36, above. See also Q. 4.96, 4.97.

(d) The use of a "pi" network for impedance matching between the plate of the output tube and the transmission line has some value in attenuating harmonic output. The output or load adjusting capacitor of the network will have much lower reactance for harmonic frequencies and thus tends to bypass such energy to ground. The diagram shown for Question 4.60 indicates the configuration for such a network.

AMPLITUDE MODULATION

Q. 3.138. What is the meaning of the term "carrier frequency"?

A. The frequency of the rf-carrier wave.

Q. 3.139. If a carrier is amplitude modulated, what causes the side-band frequencies?

A.   The process of modulation can be thought of as a process of heterodyning two or more frequencies and results in beat frequencies. The products of modulation are the two original frequencies plus the sum and difference frequencies. The sum and difference frequencies are known as the sideband frequencies. One of the two original frequencies (the radio frequency) appears unchanged and is termed the carrier frequency. The lower original or modulating frequency is also unchanged, but usually does not appear in the output of the modulated amplifier because the amplifier's load presents practically zero impedance to this low frequency.

D.   In a more analytical sense, the modulated wave is a distorted sine wave because its amplitude is varying. Mathematically it can be shown that this distorted sine wave is comprised of three component frequencies; the carrier plus the two sidebands. The amplitude of the modulated wave at any instant is the vector sum of the amplitudes of the three components at the same instant. (See also Q. 6.445, 4.43, 3.342 and 3.294.)

Q. 3.140. What determines the band-width of emission for an AM transmission?

A.   The band-width of emission for an AM transmission is always equal to twice the highest modulating frequency being used. (See also Q. 4.164.)

Q. 3.141. Why does exceeding 100% modulation in an AM transmission cause excessive bandwidth of mission?

A.   When 100% modulation is exceeded in an AM transmission, the negative peaks of the modulation envelope are clipped. The result of this is to introduce even order harmonics of the modulating frequencies into the wave. Since these represent higher modulating frequencies, the bandwidth of the emission is correspondingly increased and may become excessive.

D.   See Q. 3.343.

Q. 3.142. What is the relationship between percent modulation and the shape of the waveform "envelope" relative to carrier amplitude?

A.   The amplitude of the peaks of modulation, expressed as a percentage of the carrier amplitude, is the percentage of modulation. See Question 3.328.

Q. 3.143. Draw a simplified circuit diagram of the final stages (modulator, modulated push-pull linear amplifier) of a type of low-level

plate modulated transmitter, utilizing a pentode tube in the modulated stage. Explain the principles of operation. Repeat using a tetrode to provide high-level modulation.

A. Figure 3.143(a) illustrates one possible configuration for a low-level Class-C plate-modulated amplifier followed by a push-pull Class-B RF linear amplifier. It is believed the question is slightly in error, as a push-pull linear amplifier is not ordinarily modulated. (See Q. 6.420.)

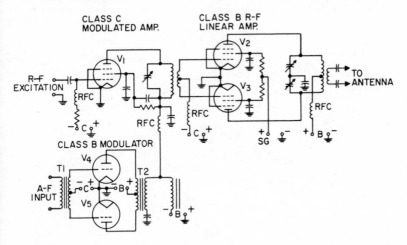

Fig. 3.143(a). Low level plate-modulated transmitter with pentode in modulated stage.

In a properly adjusted Class-C amplifier, the output voltage or amplitude is directly proportional to the applied plate voltage. Examining the diagram, it can be seen that the AF output voltage of the modulator is in series with the applied d–c plate voltage to the modulated amplifier. This results in an applied voltage that varies in accordance with the modulating frequency and therefore results in an output from the modulated amplifier whose amplitude also varies in accordance with the modulating frequency. Thus an amplitude modulated wave is created.

When a pentode is used as a modulated Class-C amplifier, it is necessary to vary the applied screen grid voltage in the same manner as the applied plate voltage. One way of doing this is shown in the figure. An inspection of the figure will reveal that the screen voltage is obtained, through a series dropping resistor, from the applied voltage and therefore both voltages will vary simultaneously.

In the circuit shown, a Class-B RF linear amplifier amplifies the already modulated wave. It is necessary to use this particular type of amplifier to prevent distortion of the modulated wave. Such an amplifier has the ability to produce an output voltage that almost exactly duplicates the exciting voltage within certain limits. A Class-C amplifier used in this position, of course, would produce intolerable distortion.

Figure 3.143(b) illustrates one possible configuration for a high level plate modulated amplifier using a tetrode. High level modulation is defined as plate modulation of the final power amplifier, hence, in this case, the output of the modulated amplifier is fed directly to the antenna instead of to a following amplifier.

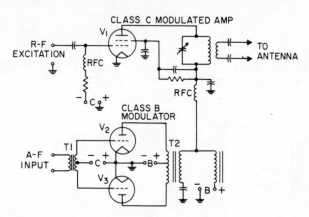

Fig. 3.143(b). High level plate-modulated transmitter with tetrode in modulated stage.

The illustrated circuit operates exactly as described for the foregoing pentode modulated amplifier. An examination of both circuits will reveal that they are similar in all respects except for the suppressor grid connection.

Q. 3.144. How does a linear power amplifier differ from other types?

A. It is assumed that the question was meant to be "How does an RF linear power amplifier differ from other types of RF power amplifiers?"

Under the above assumption, the most generally used RF power amplifier is the Class-C amplifier with its high distortion produced by using a bias voltage greatly in excess of the cut-off value. As opposed to this, the RF linear power amplifier is a Class-B amplifier that uses a bias approximately equal to the projected cut-off bias. Biased in this manner, such an amplifier has an output voltage that is almost exactly directly in proportion to the exciting voltage—hence the name, linear.

Occasionally, Class-A RF power amplifiers are used. These amplifiers are also linear, but are not able to generate the amount of output power that the Class-B amplifiers can, nor do they operate as efficiently. (See also Q. 6.420.)

Q. 3.145. Draw a simple schematic diagram showing a method of coupling a modulator tube to a radio frequency power amplifier tube to produce grid modulation of the amplified RF energy. Compare some advantages or disadvantages of this system of modulation with those of plate modulation.

A. For the diagram of the method requested, refer to the figure shown for Question 3.332.

Some *advantages* of grid modulation vs. plate modulation are as follows:

(a) The amount of audio power required of the modulator for 100% modulation is extremely small.

(b) Very much smaller modulation transformer may be used.

Some *disadvantages* of grid vs. plate modulation are as follows:

(a) The grid modulated amplifier must use tubes having an output rating approximately equal to four times the carrier output power, whereas the plate modulated amplifier must use tubes having an output rating equal to approximately one and a half times the carrier output power. The output power ratings mentioned are those for straight Class-C unmodulated or oscillator service.

(b) Distortionless modulation, greater than about 85%, is very difficult to achieve, whereas with the plate modulated amplifier, 100% modulation without distortion is easily accomplished.

Q. 3.146. What is meant by "frequency shift" or "dynamic instability?" with reference to a modulated RF emission?

A. See Question 3.333.

Q. 3.147. What would cause a dip in the antenna current when AM is applied? What are the causes of carrier shift?

A. See Questions 3.346, 3.378, 3.379 and 3.384.

Q. 3.148. What is the relationship between the average power output of the modulator and the plate circuit input of the modulated amplifier under 100 percent sinusoidal plate modulation? How does this differ when normal voice modulation is employed?

A. With 100 percent sinusoidal plate modulation, the average audio output power of the modulator is equal to 50 percent of the d–c plate circuit input power of the modulated amplifier.

With normal voice modulation, the average percentage of modulation is only in the order of 30 percent or less. This is due to the ratio of peak to average power in the human voice. Under these conditions, the average power output of the modulator is only about 4.5 percent of the amplifier's d–c plate input power. To reproduce the peaks of speech faithfully, however, the modulator must still have the same peak power capability as when called upon to produce 100% sinusoidal modulation.

Q. 3.149. What is the relationship between the amount of power in the sidebands and the intelligibility of the signal at the receiver?

A. Since all the intelligence in an amplitude-modulated emission is contained in the sidebands and none in the carrier, the intelligibility of the signal at the receiver is directly proportional to the amount of power in the sidebands.

Q. 3.150. What might cause FM in an AM radiotelephone transmitter?

A. See Question 3.333.

Q. 3.151. Draw a block diagram of an AM transmitter.

A. See the figure.

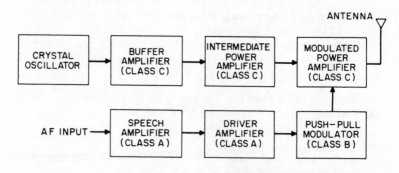

Fig. 3.151. Block diagram of an AM transmitter.

Q. 3.152. Explain the principles involved in single-sideband suppressed-carrier (SSSC) emission. How does its bandwidth of emission and required power compare with that of full carrier and sidebands?

A. Either a mathematical or electrical analysis of an amplitude modulated wave will demonstrate that the carrier of the wave is completely unaffected by the presence or absence of modulation. Further analysis will demonstrate that *each* sideband will contain *all* the intelligence that is being transmitted. The foregoing facts lead to the conclusion, that, to successfully convey intelligence, it is only necessary to transmit but one sideband; the carrier and the remaining sideband being suppressed or not transmitted.

Since, with the single-sideband suppressed-carrier (SSSC) mode of transmission, only one sideband is transmitted, the bandwidth of emission is reduced to only one half of the bandwidth required for normal amplitude-modulated transmission. The bandwidth required is equal to the highest modulating frequency used.

The signal-to-noise power ratio at the output of a radio receiver depends on several factors, among which are the following:

(1) The amount of power contained in the sidebands of the received wave.

(2) The width of the receiver's passband or its selectivity.

(3) The amount of noise power received by the antenna.

If the amount of noise power and factors *not* mentioned above are considered constant, then, for the same peak-power capabilities of the transmitter, an improvement in signal-to-noise power ratio of eight times can be obtained by the use of SSSC. For the same signal-to-noise performance at the receiver, the transmitter must be capable of handling only one eighth the peak power that would be required of an amplitude-modulated transmitter.

On an average-power, instead of a peak-power basis, the SSSC transmitter must deliver only one sixth the amount of average power required of an amplitude-modulated transmitter for the same signal-to-noise performance at the receiver.

Q. 3.153. Draw a block diagram of an SSSC transmitter (filter type) with a 20-kc oscillator and emission frequencies in the range of 6 mc. Explain the function of each stage.

A. See the figure.

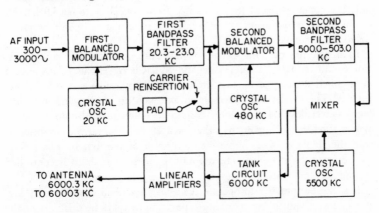

Fig. 3.153. Block diagram of a filter-type SSSC transmitter.

D. The *First Balanced Modulator,* because of special circuit balancing, produces a modulated wave containing upper and lower sidebands but no carrier. The carrier, if it were present, would have a frequency in this case of 20 kc and is supplied by the 20-kc *Crystal Oscillator.* The output of the first balanced modulator consists of the lower sideband frequencies, from 17.3 kc to 19.7 kc, and the upper sideband frequencies, from 20.3 kc to 23.0 kc.

The *First Bandpass Filter* is so designed as to pass only frequencies of 20.3 to 23.0 kc. Frequencies outside this pass band are greatly attenuated. Therefore, the first bandpass filter allows only the upper sideband frequencies to pass through and be fed to the *Second Balanced Modulator.* By this action, a single-sideband suppressed-carrier signal has been generated, but it requires further treatment as it is not of the desired frequency range as yet.

The second balanced modulator differs from the first balanced modulator only in having an input carrier frequency of 480 kc instead of 20 kc. The output of the second balanced modulator consists of lower sideband frequencies of from 457.0 kc to 459.7 kc and upper sideband frequencies of from 500.3 kc to 503.0 kc.

The second bandpass filter, because of its pass band of 500.0 kc to 503.0 kc, allows only the upper sidebands of the second balanced modulator to be presented to the input of the *Mixer.*

The mixer stage is similar to mixer stages used in superheterodyne receivers and its output consists of the original input frequencies of from 500.3 to 503.0 kc, the *Crystal Oscillator* frequency of 5500 kc, the difference frequencies from 4997.0 kc to 4999.7 kc and the sum frequencies from 6000.3 kc to 6003.0 kc.

The *Tank Circuit,* which actually is part of the mixer, is adjusted to be resonant at 6000 kc. Consequently, the output of the tank circuit is only the upper sideband frequencies of from 6000.3 kc to 6003.0 kc. All of the other responses of the mixer are discriminated against or attenuated by the tank circuit.

In actual practice, the carrier is not always suppressed completely. For use in receiving a single-sideband signal it is very useful to have a very much attenuated carrier present in the wave as a reference frequency. The carrier may be reduced as much as 20 db below the sideband power level. Propagation conditions may often dictate a carrier power level that is higher than the usual 20 db. The carrier is reinserted into the single-sideband signal at the output of the first bandpass filter as shown in the diagram. The amount of carrier reinserted is controlled by the adjustable attenuating pad.

It is normal practice to operate the above-described stages at very low power levels and to use receiving type vacuum tubes in this part of the transmitter. Today, semi-conductors are beginning to replace vacuum tubes. The section of the transmitter just described is called various names, among which are "Exciter," "SSB Generator," etc., and has a final power output in the order of tenths of a watt.

The output of an exciter is insufficient to excite the antenna and further amplification is required. Since the signal is already modulated, the normal Class C amplifier cannot be used for this purpose. Therefore, Class B RF Linear amplifiers are used to obtain essentially distortionless power amplification to the power level required at the antenna. In some infrequent instances, Class A RF Linear amplifiers are used, but this practice is rapidly declining because of the low efficiency of this class of amplifier.

Q. 3.154. Explain briefly, how an SSSC emission is detected.

A. A receiver designed for operation with SSSC transmissions differs from the ordinary receiver only in the manner of detecting the SSSC transmission. Essentially, a very accurate local oscillator's output is mixed with the IF input to the final detector. If the frequency of the local oscillator is made exactly equal to the frequency of the missing carrier, and is of the proper level, a resulting amplitude modulated wave will be generated. This amplitude modulated wave may be detected by a diode detector in the normal manner.

D. To ensure the accurate reproduction of the carrier frequency, AFC is normally employed to control the frequency of one of the preceding mixer oscillators. As stated in the preceding question, a reduced carrier is very often transmitted with the single-sideband signal to act as a reference frequency for the AFC. In this manner, the relationship between the sideband frequencies and the reinserted carrier can be maintained correctly and thus achieve the correct intelligence frequencies in the output of the final detector. It is usual to extract the reduced carrier from the final IF signal by means of a very sharp crystal filter. The extracted carrier can then be amplified or *reconditioned* and reinserted into the IF input of the final detector. This will assure the correct relationships between the carrier and the sideband frequencies. The reconditioned carrier can also be used as a reference for the AFC system and thus assure the accurate tuning of the receiver despite changes, or drifts, in any of the oscillators of the transmitter and the receiver.

Q. 3.155. Draw a block diagram of a single-conversion superheterodyne AM receiver. Assume an incident signal and explain briefly what occurs in each stage.

A. For the diagram, see Q. 3.512.
Using the incident frequency of 2450 kc as shown in the diagram, a brief description of what occurs in each stage is as follows:

1. The signal, with a frequency of 2450 kc, is fed by the antenna system into the RF amplifier where it is amplified and separated, to some extent, from other frequencies.

2. The mixer has two signals fed to it. One of these is the incoming signal of 2450 kc from the RF amplifier and the other is a signal of 2905 kc from the local oscillator. The mixer combines these two frequencies and produces in its output, the two original frequencies and their sum and differences. These are shown in the diagram.

3. The 1st IF amplifier is tuned, in this case, to 455 kc and so amplifies the 455-kc output of the mixer and rejects the remaining output frequencies. The selectivity characteristics of the IF amplifiers are such as to provide the main selectivity of the receiver.

4. The 2nd IF amplifier provides further amplification and selectivity for the 455-kc IF signal and presents it to the 2nd detector.

5. The 2nd detector demodulates the 455-kc IF signal and extracts the original audio frequencies from it. The 2nd detector usually derives a DC voltage from the carrier for use in the automatic-gain controlled stages of the receiver.

6. The audio amplifier raises the power level of the audio frequencies from the 2nd detector to a value sufficient to drive the loud speaker of the receiver.

Q. 3.156. Explain the relation between the signal frequency, oscillator frequency and the image frequency in a superheterodyne receiver.

A. See Q. 3.354.

Q. 3.157. Draw a circuit diagram of an AM second detector and AF amplifier (in one envelope), showing AVC circuitry. Also show coupling to, and identification of, all adjacent stages.

(a) Explain the principles of operation.

(b) State some conditions under which readings of AVC voltage would be helpful in trouble-shooting a receiver.

(c) Show how this circuit would be modified to give DAVC.

A. For the diagram, see Q. 6.587.

(a) For a description of operation, see Q. 3.353.

(b) The amount of AVC voltage developed is approximately proportional to the signal strength expressed in db. The AVC voltage, therefore, can be a guide in determining the amplification of all the stages preceding the 2nd detector. For example, with a relatively strong input signal the AVC voltage should be relatively large. If not, there is the possibility of weak tubes, mistuned circuits, etc., in the amplifiers ahead of the 2nd detector. In aligning a superheterodyne receiver, advantage is taken of the AVC voltage by using it as a tuning indicator. In another example of a *dead* receiver, the presence of AVC voltage but no audio output would indicate troubles in the audio frequency amplifier(s) of the receiver. This of course could be defective AF tubes or components or both.

(c) To obtain delayed automatic volume control (DAVC), it will be necessary to change the 2nd detector circuit of Q. 6.587 to that shown in the accompanying figure. This requires the addition of C_x and R_x,

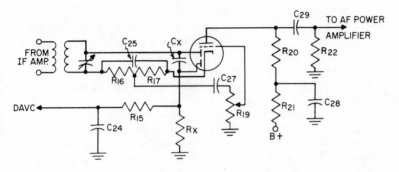

Fig. 3.157(c). Fig. 6.587 (main book) modified to provide delayed AVC.

and utilizes the lower diode exclusively for generation of a delayed AVC voltage. The upper diode is used only for detection.

Q. 3.158. Draw a BFO circuit diagram and explain its use in detection.

A. For the diagram, see the accompanying figure. For the explanation, see Q. 6.534.

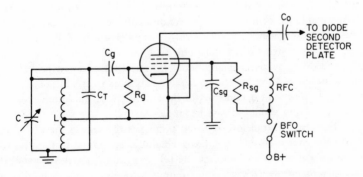

Fig. 3.158. Schematic diagram of a beat-frequency oscillator (electron-coupled Hartley).

Q. 3.159. Explain, step-by-step, how to align an AM receiver using the following instruments. In addition discuss what is occurring during each step.

(a) Signal generator and speaker.

(b) Signal generator and oscilloscope.

(c) Signal generator and VTVM.

A.   Regardless of whether a speaker, oscilloscope, or VTVM is used, the alignment procedure remains the same. Since a sweep generator is not mentioned, the signal generator to be used will be an amplitude-modulated CW generator. It must be assumed that the generator is properly calibrated and that the receiver is drastically out of alignment. When the speaker is used, the ear is the indicating instrument and no special connections to the speaker are required.

In using an oscilloscope, there are several points at which it may be connected to monitor the demodulated signal generator signal. One convenient place would be across the voice-coil terminals of the speaker. When a VTVM is used (d–c type) it is convenient to connect it to the AVC bus or across the second detector load resistor. In the event an a–c VTVM is available, this may be connected across the speaker-voice coil terminals. If the AVC voltage is not being monitored, the AVC bus should be grounded or held at a nominal fixed bias with a battery. This prevents false indications of alignment due to AVC action. Regardless of the indicating device used, a maximum indication is the sign of proper alignment. The alignment procedure follows:

1. Connect the indicating instrument as described above and proceed with the I–F alignment. A common I–F frequency of 455 kilocycles is assumed in this case.

a. Set the generator to 455 kilocycles and connect through a small capacitor (.01 uf) to the grid of the last I–F stage and ground. Set the generator for minimum useable output and peak the primary and secondary windings for maximum indication of the instrument being used.

b. Move the generator to the grid of the next-to-last I–F stage and peak the adjustments of its transformer.

c. In a like manner, all additional I–F transformers are peaked. It will be necessary to reduce the generator output as each additional stage is aligned, to prevent overloading of the amplifiers. A minimum possible generator output should always be employed.

d. The last I–F transformer to be aligned is the one in the plate circuit of the mixer. In this case, the generator is connected to the grid of the mixer (which is not tuned to the I–F frequency). At this point it is necessary to increase the generator output to obtain a usable alignment signal.

2. After completing the I–F alignment, the R–F alignment, should

be undertaken. Connect the test oscillator between the antenna terminal and ground, using a small capacitor in series with the ungrounded lead. Proceed as follows:

a. Set the signal generator and the receiver dial to 1400 kilocycles.

b. At 1400 kilocycles first adjust the oscillator trimmer to obtain maximum indication.

Note: Do not attempt to adjust the low frequency "padder" adjustment at this time and always use the minimum possible generator output.

c. Next adjust the mixer and r–f trimmers for maximum response.

d. Tune the receiver dial and the signal generator to 600 kilocycles.

e. Adjust the oscillator and low-frequency tracking trimmer for maximum response.

f. Repeat steps a through e above to achieve the optimum alignment.

D.   What is being accomplished in each step of the alignment when tuning for maximum response, is that the circuits involved are being caused to resonate at their individual frequencies. Thus, the gain of the stages are being increased due to the increased impedance of the resonant circuits. The increased gain causes the generator signal to be amplified more, providing a greater output indication. In the case of using the AVC voltage for an indication, the greater the gain of the stages, the higher the signal applied to the AVC detector. This results in a greater negative voltage being applied to the AVC bus. (Again, a maximum response indication.)

Q. 3.160.   What would be the advantages and disadvantages of utilizing a bandpass switch on a receiver?

A.   (a) Advantages. The advantage of utilizing a bandpass switch is to reduce the I–F bandpass of a receiver. In so doing, the selectivity of the receiver is considerably improved. This characteristic is highly desirable in receiving signals from stations operating in a crowded spectrum. It permits separation, and therefore the intelligible reception of signals which might otherwise be lost in the confusion of overlapping channel signals.

(b) Disadvantages. The disadvantage of utilizing a bandpass switch is that sideband frequencies of either voice or music broadcasts will be sharply reduced, thus reducing the intelligibility of speech and music. However, in some cases using the bandpass switch is the only way to achieve any reception at all of the desired signal.

D.   By the use of regenerative I–F circuits, a controllable bandpass characteristic may be achieved. This can cut the I–F bandpass to as low as 1000 cycles for use under extremely difficult signal crowding and noise conditions. Since good double-sideband voice reproduction normally requires about a 6000 cycle bandpass, it is obvious that the intelligibility of voice (and music) will be considerably reduced. However, this technique frequently permits a signal to be received which might otherwise be covered up by interference. Since noise frequencies occupy the entire spectrum, it is seen that the sharper the bandpass, the less the noise energy that will be passed to affect the listener. In receivers used for code reception, a crystal-type I–F filter is frequently employed. With this type of filter, a bandpass of only 100 to 200 cycles is passed. This bandwidth is adequate for code, but useless for voice or music reception.

Q. 3.161. Explain sensitivity and selectivity of a receiver. Why are these important quantities? In what typical units are they usually expressed?

A. (a) Sensitivity: Sensitivity is the strength of the signal, in microvolts, at the input of the receiver required to produce a specified audio-power output.

(b) Selectivity: Selectivity is the ability of a receiver to discriminate against frequencies other than the desired frequency.

(c) Sensitivity is an important quantity because it defines the ability of a receiver to respond adequately to a weak-input signal.

(d) Selectivity defines the ability of a receiver to *select* a desired signal, which may be hemmed in by adjacent frequency (undesirable) signals.

(e) Sensitivity is expressed in microvolts for a certain audio output power.

(f) Selectivity is expressed in cycles or kilocycles, usually in terms of the I–F response curve of the receiver.

FREQUENCY MODULATION

Q. 3.162. Draw a schematic diagram of a frequency-modulated oscillator using a reactance-tube modulator. Explain its principle of operation.

A. For the diagram see Q. 4.237. For the principle of operation see the discussion under Q. 4.221.

Q. 3.163. Discuss the following in reference to frequency modulation.
(a) The production of sidebands.
(b) The relationship between the number of sidebands and the modulating frequency.
(c) The relationship between the number of sidebands and the amplitude of the modulating voltage.
(d) The relationship between percent modulation and the number of sidebands.

(e) The relationship between modulation index or deviation ratio and the number of sidebands.

(f) The relationship between the spacing of the sidebands and the modulating frequency.

(g) The relationship between the number of sidebands and the bandwidth of emissions.

(h) The criteria for determining the bandwidth of emission.

(i) Reasons for pre-emphasis.

A. (a) When a sine wave is frequency modulated, its *instantaneous* frequency is varied according to the intelligence to be transmitted. The modulated wave consists of components made up of the original sine wave plus additional sine waves. These additional sine waves are of different frequencies from the original wave and are called sidebands and are symmetrically arranged above and below the original wave or carrier.

(b) For a given frequency deviation, the number of sidebands is inversely proportional to the modulating frequency. For example, for a frequency deviation of plus or minus 75 kilocycles and a modulating frequency of 15,000 cycles, there will be five significant sidebands on each side of the carrier. With a modulating frequency of 150 cycles and the same deviation, there will be 500 significant sidebands on each side of the carrier.

(c) For a given modulating frequency, the number of sidebands is directly proportional to the amplitude of the modulating voltage. That is, if the modulating voltage is tripled, the number of sidebands is also tripled.

(d) In FM broadcast service, one hundred percent modulation is defined as the modulating condition producing a frequency deviation of plus or minus 75 kilocycles. The number of sidebands produced, for any given modulating frequency, is directly proportional to the percent modulation.

(e) For any given modulating frequency, the number of significant sidebands is directly proportional to the modulation index and, for a linearly modulated transmitter, is also proportional to the deviation ratio.

(f) The sidebands produced by frequency modulation are separated from one another by a frequency that is equal to the modulating frequency. The sidebands adjacent to the carrier are also separated from it by an amount equal to the modulating frequency.

(g) The total number of significant sidebands multiplied by the modulating frequency equals the total significant bandwidth of emission. There are sidebands extending beyond this, but they are insignificant and contain so little power or energy that they are considered negligible.

(h) The criteria for determining the bandwidth of emission are the modulation index and the modulating frequency. The product of the modulation index and the frequency of modulation equals the frequency deviation. The bandwidth of emission is twice the sum of the frequency deviation and the modulating frequency.

(i) In speech and music very little energy is contained in the frequencies at the upper end of the audio frequency range. However, even though such components represent very little energy, they are extremely important to the naturalness of speech as they give *definition* to the consonants and add to the identification of the different types of musical instruments. Normally, these high frequency components will be lost in transmission because of *masking* by noise unless some way is found to make them override such circuit noise. One way of accomplishing this is to amplify these components more than the low frequency sounds before introducing the complete audio signal to the modulating circuits of the FM transmitter. This process is termed *pre-emphasis*—that is, the high frequencies are emphasized before modulation and thus represent more energy during transmission. At the receiver, in order to restore these components to their original amplitude relationship with the low-frequency components, it is necessary to reverse the process after detection. This latter process is termed *de-emphasis*. See Q. 4.222, 4.223.

Q. 3.164.   How is good stability of a reactance tube modulator achieved?

A.   In addition to the stability achieved by normal good design of the self-excited oscillator employed as a reactance tube modulated oscillator, further stability is obtained by operating the oscillator at a low radio frequency. The oscillator's operating frequency is at an integral submultiple of the desired antenna frequency. The oscillator is followed by frequency multipliers sufficient to obtain the desired final frequency.

A further advantage in stability is gained by operating the oscillator at a low frequency. This is because the frequency deviation, and hence the modulation index, is multiplied by the same factor as the carrier frequency when the signal is passed through frequency multiplying stages. Because of the low frequency deviation required, the effect of the reactance tube modulator on the stability of the oscillator is decreased.

D.   Any self-excited oscillator, no matter how carefully designed is subject to some frequency drift. In addition, any variation in the parameters of the reactance tube will cause the oscillator to change frequency. To insure a completely stable reactance tube and oscillator, it is customary to employ an AFC system whose reference is an extremely stable crystal oscillator. A simplified block diagram of such an AFC system is shown in the illustration. The phase detector receives signals (divided in frequency) from both the crystal oscillator and the self-excited oscillator. The two signals are compared in the phase detector. If the fre-

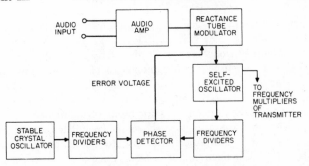

Fig. 3.164. Simplified block diagram of an AFC system used to stabilize a reactance-tube modulator.

quency of the self-excited oscillator differs from that of the crystal oscillator, the phase detector develops a d–c error voltage which is fed to the reactance-tube modulator. This error voltage is of the correct polarity to bring the self excited oscillator to its correct frequency. As the oscillator approaches the correct frequency, the amplitude of the error voltage will decrease to practically zero.

Q. 3.165. Draw a circuit diagram of a phase modulator. Explain its operation. Label adjacent stages.

A.   For the diagram, refer to the figure.

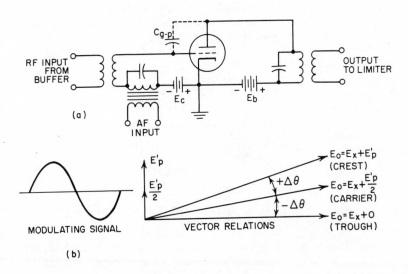

Fig. 3.165. Phase modulator schematic diagram.

The stage shown in the diagram is a grid-modulated Class A or Class C modulator operated at a sufficiently low stage gain to prevent oscillation from feedback through the grid-plate interlectrode capacitance, $C_{g\text{-}p}$. This may be accomplished by a combination of relatively low E_b and low tank circuit resonant impedance. The modulated output voltage of the stage appears across the tank circuit and will vary, during modulation, according to the instantaneous amplitude of the modulating signal. For simplicity, the vector diagram shows the modulated output voltage varying from zero to twice the carrier or zero modulation voltage. This amounts to 100% modulation, but in practice the modulation percentage need not be as high.

Appearing across the tank is another voltage, E_x, resulting from direct feedthrough via $C_{g\text{-}p}$. This voltage, because of the reactance of this capacitance, is very nearly 90° out of phase with the modulator output voltage. The total voltage across the tank is the vector sum of these two voltages. The instantaneous phase, can be seen to vary from the reference or carrier condition in accordance with the amplitude of the modulator output. Since this is a function of the modulating signal, the instantaneous phase of the wave varies with the instantaneous amplitude of the modulating signal.

Q. 3.166.   Explain what occurs in a waveform if it is phase modulated.

A.   When a sine wave is phase modulated it becomes a distorted sine wave as illustrated in an exaggerated manner in the accompanying figure. As a result of this distortion, additional frequencies are created and appear in the modulated wave as sidebands.

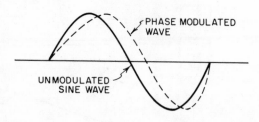

Fig. 3.166. Effect of phase modulation on a sine wave.

Since frequency may be expressed as the rate of change of phase, the instantaneous frequency of the modulated wave is varied in exact accordance with the variation in the rate of change of phase. The net result of the foregoing is that phase modulation produces the same sort of modulated wave that is produced by frequency modulation. Actually, for the same modulating frequency and modulation index, the two waves will be identical.

Q. 3.167. Explain, in a general way, why an FM deviation meter (modulation meter) would show an indication if coupled to the output of a transmitter which is phase-modulated by a constant amplitude; constant audio frequency. To what would this deviation be proportional?

A.   Since a phase-modulated transmitter produces a wave that is frequncy modulated, as explained in Q. 3.166 above, an FM deviation meter would show an indication because frequency deviation would in fact exist.

The amount of such deviation will be proportional to the amplitude *and* the frequency of the modulating signal, whereas the deviation in an FM transmitter is proportional only to the amplitude of the modulating signal and is independent of its frequency.

Q. 3.168.   Draw a circuit diagram of each of the following stages of a phase-modulated FM transmitter. Explain their operation. Label adjacent stages.

(a) Frequency multiplier (doubler) with capacitive coupling on input and output.

(b) Power amplifier with variable link coupling to antenna. Include circuit for metering grid and plate currents.

(c) Speech amplifier with an associated pre-emphasis circuit.

A.   For the diagrams, see the accompanying figure.

The operation of the frequency doubler is explained in Q. 3.138. The degree of coupling to the intermediate power amplifier can be varied by changing the position of the tap on the coil or by changing the value of the output capacitor. Moving the tap toward the ground end of the tank coil will reduce the amount of coupling.

The operation of the power amplifier is explained under the discussion of Q. 3.104. The degree of coupling to the antenna can be varied by changing the position of the small coil with respect to the tank coil. The tuned circuit at the other end of the link is resonated to the operatting frequency. The taps on this coil are adjusted to match the required input impedance of the transmission line to the antenna itself.

The speech amplifier as shown is a Class A transformer-coupled stage and its operation is described in Q. 3.106. Following the amplifier is a network to provide pre-emphasis of the higher audio frequencies. Details of this network and its operation may be found in Q. 4.222.

Q. 3.169.   Discuss wide-band and narrow-band reception in FM voice communication systems with respect to frequency deviation and bandwidth.

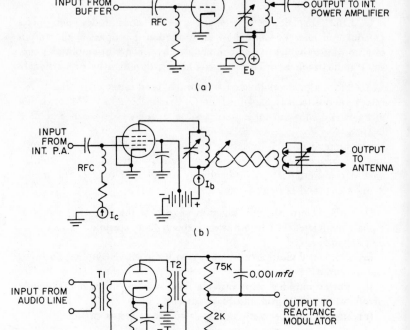

Fig. 3.168. Different stages of a phase-modulated FM transmitter: (a) frequency doubler; (b) power amplifier; (c) speech amplifier.

A. See Q. 3.495 for discussion.

Q. 3.170. What might be the effect on the transmitted frequency if a tripler stage in an otherwise perfectly aligned FM transmitter, were slightly de-tuned?

A. The tank circuit of such a tripler would present a reactive impedance to the plate of the tube instead of a resistive impedance. The value of such a reactive impedance and the resulting phase angle will depend on the frequency at any instant. Since the instantaneous frequency varies during modulation, the detuned tripler stage will inject an additional phase modulation component into the frequency modulated wave. When such a wave is finally detected at the receiver the additional frequencies will be present at the output along with the original frequencies. Such unwanted frequencies represent interference and noise.

Q. 3.171. Could the harmonic of an FM transmission contain intelligible modulation?

A. The harmonics of FM transmission do contain intelligible modulation, the only difference between them and the fundamental is the increased deviation. The deviation is multiplied by the order of the harmonic.

Q. 3.172. Under what usual conditions of maintenance and/or repair should a transmitter be retuned?

A. If tubes, RF components or RF leads are involved or disturbed during maintenance or repair, the transmitter should be retuned. Maintenance and/or repair of the power and control circuits normally do not require such retuning.

Q. 3.173. If an indirect FM transmitter without modulation was within carrier frequency tolerance, but with modulation out of tolerance, what would be some possible causes?

A. In the indirect or Armstrong system of frequency modulation, the actual modulation is obtained by employing a balanced modulator to produce side bands, only, to be combined with the carrier only after the carrier has been shifted in phase by $90°$. The carrier, during modulation, is defined as the average frequency of the whole spectrum emitted. The most probable cause of the average frequency being out of tolerance during modulation is the balanced modulator not being balanced. Such an event would result in the production of unequal sidebands which would have the effect of shifting the average frequency upward or downward. Without modulation, the average frequency or carrier would be unchanged in frequency because the sidebands being added to it at this time are zero.

Q. 3.174. In an FM transmitter what would be the effect on antenna current if the grid bias on the final power amplifier were varied?

A. Normally, the final power amplifier of an FM transmitter is operated Class C. With such an amplifier, a change in its grid bias will produce a change in its output power and hence a change in the antenna current. Usually, a decrease in grid bias will increase the power output with an attendant increase in antenna current. An increase in grid bias will have just the opposite effect. Both of these effects can take place only over a rather limited range.

Q. 3.175. Explain briefly, the principles involved in frequency-shift keying (FSK). How is this signal detected?

A.   The basic principles involved in frequency-shift keying are discussed in Q. 6.482. Such a signal may be detected at the receiver by means of a discriminator such as that used for FM. However, such a discriminator must use a DC coupled audio output to provide a DC output when the keying is stopped on either *space* or *mark*.

Q. 3.176.   Assume you have available the following instruments:

> AC-DC VTVM
> Ammeter
> Heterodyne frequency meter (.0002% accuracy).
> Absorption wave meter
> FM modulation meter

Draw and label a block diagram of a voice modulated (press-to-talk microphone), indirect (phase modulated) PM transmitter having a crystal multiplication of 12.

(a)   If the desired output frequency were 155.460 mc., what would be the proper crystal frequency?

(b)   Consider the transmitter strip completely de-tuned; there are ammeter jacks in the control grid circuits of the multipliers and the control grid and cathode circuits of the final circuits of the final amplifier. Explain, in detail, step-by-step, a proper procedure for tuning and aligning all stages except plate circuit of final power amplifier (PA).

(c)   Assume a tunable antenna with adjustable coupling to the plate circuit of the final PA. With the ammeter in the cathode circuit of the PA and with the aid of a tube manual, describe a step-by-step method of obtaining maximum output power, without damage to the tube.

(d)   If the PA in (c) above were a pentode how would you determine the power input to the stage?

(e)   In (c) above how would you determine if the PA stage were self-oscillating; if so, what adjustments could be made?

(f)   Assume the transmitter's assigned frequency is 155.460 mc., with a required tolerance of plus or minus 0.0005 percent. What would be the minimum and maximum frequencies, as read on the frequency meter, which would assure the transmitter being within tolerance?

(g)   Assume the 1 mc crystal oscillator of the frequency meter has been calibrated with WWV and that the meter is tunable to any frequency between each 1 mc interval over a range of 20-40 mc, with usable harmonics up to 640 mc. Explain in detail what connections and adjustments would be made to measure the signal directly from the transmitter; also by means of a receiver.

(h)   If in checking the frequency deviation with the modulation meter, would you expect the greatest deviation by whistling or by speaking in a low voice into the microphone?

(i) If the transmitter contained a means for limiting, and were over-modulating, what measurements and adjustments could be made to determine and remedy the fault?

A.   For the block diagram, see the accompanying figure.

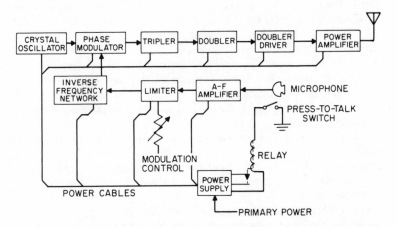

Fig. 3.176.   Block diagram of a voice-modulated, phase-modulated
FM transmitter.

(a) Since the transmitter employs a frequency multiplication of 12, the proper crystal frequency is the desired output frequency of 155.460 mc divided by 12 or 12.955 mc.

(b) It is assumed that the ammeter available is actually a milliammeter and is capable of being fitted with a pair of leads terminating in a suitable plug for use in measuring electrode currents in the stages by means of the jacks available. It is further assumed that the crystal oscillator is an electron-coupled Pierce oscillator.

In aligning the transmitter it is first necessary to remove the plate and screen voltages from the power amplifier. The power is then applied to the preceding stages by operating the *Press-to-Talk* switch.

The plate circuit of the oscillator is tuned to resonance by adjusting for maximum grid current in the tripler stage. At this point check the frequency of the oscillator by loosely coupling the wavemeter to the oscillator plate coil. The frequency, by this method of measurement, should be approximately 13 mc. This measurement is to assure us that the oscillator plate coil is tuned to the fundamental and not to a second or even third harmonic. This is possible in some cases due to the range of frequencies for which some oscillators are designed.

If the heterodyne frequency meter available can measure frequencies in this range, it its advisable to measure the exact frequency of the oscillator by loosely coupling the frequency meter to the oscillator plate coil. If this measurement is not feasible, the final output frequency of the transmitter can be measured later.

The milliammeter is next inserted in the jack in the control grid circuit of the first doubler and the plate circuit of the tripler adjusted for maximum grid current for this stage. Again, it is necessary to couple the wavemeter loosely to the plate coil of the tripler and check to see if the tripler output frequency approximates 39 mc. This is to assure the stage is actually tripling the frequency and not doubling or quadrupling it.

The first doubler is adjusted in a similar fashion, again tuning for maximum grid current in the following stage. The wavemeter in this case should indicate approximately 78 mc as the output frequency for this stage.

The procedure is again followed for the second doubler and the wavemeter used to be certain that its output is approximately 155 mc. At this point, more than normal grid current should be indicated by the milliammeter which is inserted in the jack for the control-grid current of the power amplifier.

(c) With the preceding stages of the transmitter aligned as in (b) above, and the coupling to the antenna has been reduced to the minimum the plate and screen voltages to the power amplifier can be restored.

As soon as the power is applied to the transmitter, by operating the press-to-talk switch, the plate tank of the power amplifier must be adjusted for minimum cathode current. Following this, the antenna must be resonated as indicated by a maximum rise in cathode current. If little or no effect can be noted on the cathode current, it will be necessary to increase the antenna coupling slightly. When tuning the antenna results in a noticeable peak in cathode current, the cathode current and the grid current should be noted and the tube manual consulted. If the cathode current and the grid current are as specified by the tube manual, then the power amplifier will be delivering its maximum output power.

It should be borne in mind that the cathode current is the sum of the control grid, screen and plate currents. The control grid current can be measured independently by means of the jack in the grid circuit. If the applied screen and plate voltages are known, the screen current can be estimated from the information in the tube manual. The plate current can also be estimated with a fair amount of accuracy.

If the currents thus obtained are not sufficient, according to the tube manual, the coupling to the antenna should be increased in small increments until the desired screen and plate currents are realized without excessive grid current. After each change of coupling it will be necessary to retune the plate tank of the power amplifier to resonance as indicated by minimum cathode current. It is quite often advisable to check the tuning of the doubler driver at the same time.

(d) Since the input power to the power amplifier is the product of its plate current and its applied plate voltage, it is necessary to measure these quantities. The cathode current and the grid current can be measured with the aid of the milliammeter. If the applied screen and plate potentials are not given in the instruction manual they can be measured with the aid of the VTVM. From a tube manual, the screen current can be estimated and it and the grid current subtracted from the cathode current, leaving the amount of plate current. Since the screen current is usually only a small fraction of the plate current, this will make the plate current known to a fair degree of accuracy. If greater accuracy is desired and the screen voltage is obtained across a series dropping resistor of known value, the voltage drop across the resistor can be measured with the VTVM and the screen current determined by Ohm's law.

The power input to the stage can then be found by multiplying the plate current by the applied plate potential.

(e) Self-oscillation of the power amplifier can be detected by removing the tube in the tripler and noting the effect on the grid and cathode currents in the power amplifier. If sufficient fixed bias is used in the power amplifier to cut-off the plate and screen currents in the absence of excitation, removal of the tripler tube should result in such currents being zero. If the stage is oscillating, plate and screen currents will continue to flow in the absence of excitation.

If the power amplifier is a triode, neutralizing arrangements exist. To rid the stage of self-oscillation, the neutralizing adjustments must be performed. The exact nature of such adjustments will depend on just what type of neutralizing facilities are provided.

If the stage uses a pentode or beam power tube, conditions sometimes will cause self-oscillation. Usually, insufficient loading is the cause and increasing the loading on the stage by closer coupling to the antenna will make the circuit behave more normally.

Grid and plate currents should rise and fall smoothly as the plate circuit is tuned through resonance. Erratic behavior of these currents indicate at least a tendency toward self-oscillation.

(f) Using the available frequency meter with its accuracy of plus or minus 0.0002%, it will be necessary to subtract this accuracy from the tolerance of plus or minus 0.0005% to be absolutely certain the transmitter frequency is within tolerance. Under these conditions, multiplying the carrier frequency of 155.460 mc by plus or minus 0.0003% gives an allowable variation in frequency, as read on the meter of plus or minus 0.0004664 mc. The maximum frequency would be 155.4604664 mc and the minimum 155.4595336 mc, as read on the frequency meter.

(g) It is assumed, further, that the detector of the frequency meter is also tunable only over the range of 20-40 mc. If this is so, then the meter input should be coupled to the plate coil of the transmitter's tripler and the detector (oscillating) adjusted to zero beat with the tripler's output.

The detector is then adjusted to pick up the 38th harmonic of the meter's 1-mc crystal and the detector's dial calibration adjusted to agree with this. The detector dial should then be varied to pick up the 39th harmonic and the calibration checked at this point. Returning to the frequency of the tripler output, the carrier may be read directly from the detector dial if so calibrated or interpolated if the dial is linearly divided. The frequency of the transmitter, in this case, will be four times the frequency of the tripler output (38.865×4, or 155.460 mc).

If a receiver is employed, the unmodulated transmitter is tuned in and the frequency meter's oscillating detector RF output is also coupled to the receiver. After checking the meter's calibration as described above, the detector is adjusted so its fourth harmonic is heard in the receiver at zero beat with the transmitter. The transmitter frequency, then is four times the reading as obtained on the meter's detector dial.

(h) Since this is an FM transmitter, the amount of deviation produced is dependent only on the amplitude of the modulating signal and is independent of the modulating frequency. It is assumed that whistling into the microphone produces a louder signal than when speaking in a low voice and therefore the frequency deviation should be greater when whistling.

(i) The *modulation control* shown in the accompanying diagram is used to adjust the output of the limiter stage. This control should be adjusted so that when a very loud talker is speaking into the microphone, the FM modulation meter indicates the maximum allowable frequency deviation. Assurance is then had that this deviation will not be exceeded no matter which person uses the transmitter. Care should be taken to note that when the limiter output is being *reduced* the deviation also becomes less. This makes certain that the limiter is actually limiting the maximum level of speech.

The original determination of the fault, can be made with the FM modulation meter.

Q. 3.177.   Draw a schematic diagram of each of the following stages of a superheterodyne FM receiver. Explain the principles of operation. Label adjacent stages.

(a) Mixer with injected oscillator frequency.
(b) IF amplifier.
(c) Limiter.
(d) Discriminator.
(e) Differential squelch circuit.

A.   (a) For schematic of the mixer, see the accompanying figure. This circuit is frequently referred to as a "mixer-oscillator" circuit. It uses one special type tube to perform the functions of both mixer and oscillator. The oscillator section of the tube is a triode, consisting of the

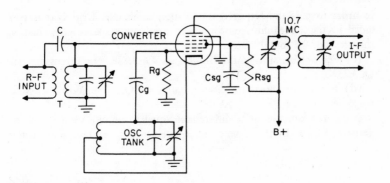

Fig. 3.177(a). Simplified schematic diagram of an FM mixer circuit with injected oscillator frequency.

control grid, cathode and screen grid. The converter section is a pentode made up of the special injector grid, cathode-screen grid, suppressor grid and plate. In this type of circuit, both the control grid (oscillator voltage) and injector grid (r–f voltage) signals are mixed electronically. Both of these signals modulate the electron stream going from cathode to plate. Since the tube is operated in a non-linear fashion, heterodyning of the two frequencies results and the desired i–f frequency of 10.7 megacycles is selected by the tuned circuit in the converter plate.

(b) For schematic of the i–f amplifier, see the accompanying figure.

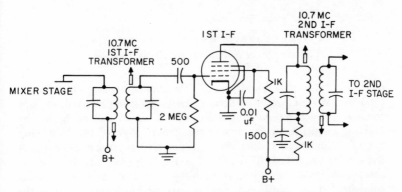

Fig. 3.177(b). Simplified schematic diagram of a first I-F amplifier stage for an FM radio.

This is a Class-A amplifier with double-tuned plate and grid circuits resonated to the center i–f of 10.7 megacycles. The bandwidth of the i–f of a broadcast FM receiver will be in the order of 150 to 200 kilocycles in order to pass the required modulation sidebands. Grid bias is provided by the 2 megohm resistor which produces a space-charge bias in the order of 0.5 to 1.0 volt.

(c) For a schematic of the limiter, see Q. 4.238. For discussion, see Q. 4.233.

(d) For a schematic of a discriminator, see Q. 4.236. For discussion, see Q. 4.217.

(e) For schematic of a differential squelch circuit, see the accompanying figure. In the absence of a receiver-input signal, considerable

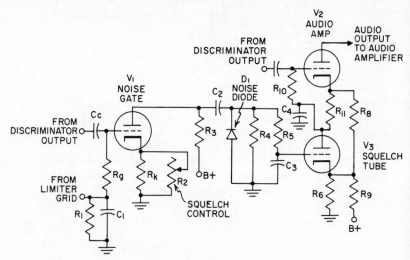

Fig. 3.177(e). Schematic diagram of a differential squelch circuit for an FM superheterodyne receiver.

noise may be amplified and heard in the speaker causing an annoying condition. With a certain minimum signal level being received, the FM receiver will achieve *quieting* and only the signal will be heard. By utilizing a squelch circuit, the no-signal "noise" is prevented from being amplified. Further, a squelch control is provided to prevent weak signals from being squelched. This control is R2 in Figure 3.177(e). In the absence of signal, the control is normally set so that the noise is barely squelched. Weak signals can then be received. However, signals in the noise level may be lost and it is sometimes desirable to operate with no squelch.

In the absence of signal, noise is amplified by the noise gate. The setting of R2 and the lack of limiter grid bias applied to R1 permits V1 to amplify normally. The amplified noise is rectified by noise diode D1 and integrated by capacitor C3. The resultant, a positive d–c voltage is applied to the grid of squelch amplifier V3, causing V3 to conduct at its maximum rate. Squelch-tube current through R11, in the cathode of V2, causes V2 to be cut off and no noise output results. When a limiting signal is received, the limiter bias cuts off V1. (Capacitor Cc in the grid of V1 is very small and normally will only pass the high-frequency noise impulses.) Further, a limiting signal prevents (from the limiter or ratio detector operation) noise from appearing at V1. Under this condition, the voltage across C3 drops to zero and V3 is cut off by the fixed cathode bias across R6. With the squelch tube cut-off, V2 operates normally and amplifies its audio input.

D. See Q. 3.492, 4.223 for additional FM receiver discussion.

Q. 3.178. Draw a diagram of a ratio detector and explain its operation.

A. For schematic and discussion of a ratio detector, see Q. 4.231.

Q. 3.179. Explain how spurious signals can be received or created in a receiver. How could this be reduced in sets having sealed untunable filters?

A. (a) Spurious signals may be received from channels adjacent to the desired one due to inadequate receiver selectivity.

(b) Spurious signals may be created in a receiver by regenerating or oscillating i–f amplifiers. They may also be generated by the two local oscillators, multipliers and mixers which may create numerous harmonic and heterodyne frequencies. (See Q. 3.180 below, for block diagram of a typical FM communications receiver.)

(c) By the use of a sealed-untunable filter it is possible to achieve an important improvement in the selectivity of the receiver and to reject many of the undesired frequencies.

D. The sealed filter is usually placed at the input to the low-frequency i–f amplifier. It has a response which is essentially flat over the necessary i–f bandwidth and which drops off very steeply (skirts) on both sides. Actually, the sealed filter establishes the i–f bandpass. The filters are sealed to avoid change due to atmospheric conditions and are designed to be relatively impervious to changes in their associated stages. See also Q. 3.497, where other interference problems are discussed.

Q. 3.180. Describe, step-by-step, a proper procedure for aligning an FM double conversion superheterodyne receiver.

A. A double-conversion (or double-superheterodyne) receiver is used to eliminate image interference (see Q. 3.265, 3.354) from stations operating within a particular band, and to provide good adjacent channel rejection. For an FM broadcast receiver (88-108 mc) the usual i–f is

10.7 mc. With this i–f, no FM broadcast image interference is possible. Therefore, it will be assumed that the FM receiver referred to in this question is not an FM broadcast receiver, but is a VHF communications-type receiver capable of operating on one or more frequency channels. A block diagram of such a receiver is given in the accompanying figure.

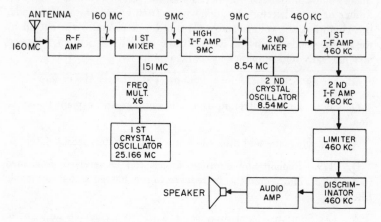

Fig. 3.180. Block diagram of a fixed-tuned, double-conversion FM superheterodyne receiver.

This is a single channel receiver, as shown, utilizing two crystal oscillators. Additional channels might be received on such a receiver by the switching of additional crystals. An input r–f signal of 160 mc is assumed. It is also assumed that the *high* i–f is 9 megacycles and the *low* i–f is 460 kilocycles. The exact frequencies chosen are typical, but not critical, as the alignment procedure applies equally well to other frequencies.

The equipment used for the alignment will be a properly calibrated CW signal generator and a zero-center VTVM. The alignment will be performed in steps beginning with the discriminator detector (not ratio detector).

(a) Alignment of the Discriminator: Connect the zero-center VTVM between the junction of the two series-output resistors and ground. Connect the signal generator output through a small capacitor to the grid of the limiter stage and ground. Set the signal generator to 460 kilocycles. The VTVM should be set to a low scale and the generator output control adjusted to give a useful meter reading. Adjust the primary of the discriminator transformer for maximum deflection of the VTVM, reducing signal-generator output if necessary. Do not change the generator connections, but move the *hot* VTVM lead to the top of the two series-output resistors. Now, tune the discriminator secondary for a zero indication (center) between two peaks (one positive and one negative). Check the output linearity by tuning the generator equal increments on both sides of the center frequency. Equal, but opposite polarities, of voltage should occur. If this is not the case, touch up the primary adjustment to bring it about. This completes the discriminator alignment.

Note: As in most alignment procedures, use the minimum possible signal-generator output.

(b) Alignment of the Limiter: Connect the VTVM between the grid of the limiter and ground. Set the meter to read a low negative voltage. Connect the signal generator (through a small capacitor) tuned to 460 kc (unmodulated), between the grid and ground of the last i–f stage preceding the mixer. The signal generator output should be the minimum possible to obtain a meter reading, in order to prevent limiter saturation which would cause broad tuning. (Maintain this low generator output throughout the entire alignment process, reducing it as necessary when the circuits come into resonance.) Now tune the secondary of the last i–f transformer for maximum meter deflection. Next, tune the primary in a similar manner.

(c) Alignment of the I–F's: (Two i–f stages are present). Maintain the meter in the limiter grid circuit. Move the signal generator (at 460 kc) to the grid of the first i–f stage (through a small capacitor). Peak first the secondary and then the primary of the i–f transformer betwen the first and second i–f stages. Next, without changing the meter position, move the signal generator (at 460 kc) to the grid of the second mixer stage (through a small capacitor). The generator output may have to be increased at this point since the second mixer grid circuit is resonated at 9 megacycles (not 460 kc). Peak the secondary and then the primary of the i–f transformer between the second mixer and first i–f stages.

(d) Set the signal generator to 160 megacycles and connect it to the antenna input of the r–f amplifier through a small capacitor. Maintain the VTVM at the grid of the limiter. As before, use the lowest possible signal-generator output. The frequency multiplier adjustments will result in the highest amplitude 151 mc signal being applied to the first mixer. This in turn will cause a 9 megacycle output from the first mixer and a 460 kilocycle output from the second mixer. Therefore, peak the multiplier adjustments for maximum VTVM readings. Next, peak the adjustments at the input and output of the *high* i–f amplifier. Following this, peak the adjustments at the input and output of the r–f amplifier. This completes the alignment procedure.

In the event the receiver has several channels, obtained by crystal switching, the *front-end* alignment will be slightly different. In this event, the r–f amplifier and first mixer will be somewhat broadbanded and tuned to the center of the channels. Selectivity will be provided by the i-f amplifiers, as usual.

Q. 3.181.   Discuss the cause and prevention of interference to radio receivers installed in motor vehicles.

A.   See Q. 3.506.

TRANSISTORS

Q. 3.182.   Describe the difference between *positive* (P–type) and *negative* (N–type) semiconductors with respect to:
(a) The direction of current flow when an external emf is applied.
(b) The internal resistance when an external emf is applied.

A.   (a) In P–type semiconductors, the major-current carriers are *holes* (positive charges). Hole current within the semiconductor moves from the end connected to the positive battery terminal to the end connected to the negative battery terminal. In N–type semiconductors, the majority current carriers are electrons. Electron current within the semiconductor moves from the end connected to the negative battery terminal to the end connected to the positive battery terminal.

(b) In both the P and N–types, the internal resistance may be considered to be low in the direction of the majority current carriers and high in the opposite direction.

Q. 3.183.   What is the difference between forward and reverse biasing of transistors?

A.   (a) When a transistor junction is *forward* biased, a continuous current flows through the junction due to the movement of the majority carriers through the P and N–type material. (Holes in P type and electrons in N–type constitute the majority carriers.) Fig. 3.528 illustrates forward biasing of the emitter-base junction and reverse biasing of the collector-base junction.

(b) Reverse biasing of a transistor junction in effect prevents current from flowing in that junction. In practice a small current (in microamperes) will flow in the junction due to the movement of minority carriers. Minority carriers consist of a relatively small number of excess holes found in N–type crystals and a relatively small number of excess electrons in P–type crystals. It should be noted that the conditions of forward and reverse biasing are normal operating conditions as shown in Q. 3.528. This shows a PNP transistor. For an NPN transistor, both battery polarities would be reversed. (See also Q. 3.26 Sup. No. 1.)

D.   Forward and reverse biasing terminology may also be applied to the base-to-emitter bias of a transistor. In this case, forward biasing of a transistor means that the bias polarity from base-to-emitter is such as to permit relatively large current flow from the emitter to the collector.

Note: For a PNP–type the base is made negative with respect to the emitter. Opposite polarity bias is used for an NPN–type.

In this same general case, reverse bias means that the base-to-emitter bias is such as to prevent emitter to collector current flow (except for leakage current).

Note: For a PNP–type the base is now made positive with respect to the emitter. Opposite polarity bias is used for an NPN–type.

Q. 3.184. Show connections of external batteries, resistance load and signal source as would appear in a properly (fixed) biased common-emitter transistor amplifier.

A.   See the figure.

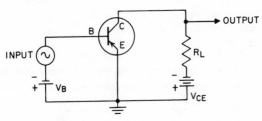

Fig. 3.184. Schematic diagram of a PNP common-emitter transistor amplifier using fixed bias batteries.

Q. 3.185. The following are excerpts from a transistor handbook describing the characteristics of a PNP alloy-type transistor as used in a common-emitter circuit configuration. Explain the significance of each item.

Maximum and Minimum Ratings:
(a) Collector-to-base voltage (emitter open)   — 40 max. volts
(b) Collector-to-emitter voltage
     (Base-to-emitter volts = 0.5) .... — 40 max. volts
(c) Emitter-to-base voltage .... — 0.5 max. volts
(d) Collector current .... 10 max. ma
Transistor Dissipation:
(e) At ambient temperature of 25° C
     For operation in free air .... 120 max. ma
(f) At case temperature of 25° C
     For operation with heat sink .... 140 max. ma
(g) Ambient-temperature range:
     Operating and storage .... — 65 to + 100°C

A.   (a) Collector-to-Base Voltage: The maximum voltage which can be applied between these elements without danger of a breakdown of the collector-to-base junction.

(b) Collector-to-Emitter Voltage: The maximum safe voltage which can be applied between collector and emitter (with a reverse bias of 0.5 volt between base and emitter), without breakdown occurring from collector-to-emitter.

(c) Emitter-to-Base Voltage: The maximum safe forward-bias voltage, to limit emitter-to-collector current and base-to-emitter current.

(d) Collector Current: The maximum permissable collector current at which the transistor may be operated without adverse effects.

(e) Transistor Dissipation in Free Air: The maximum safe thermal rating at which the transistor may be operated without a heat sink.

(f) Transistor Dissipation with Heat Sink: The maximum safe thermal rating at which the transistor may be operated with a heat sink.

(g) Ambient-Temperature Range: The design limits for ambient temperature operation or storage of the transistor.

Q. 3.186.   Draw a circuit diagram of a method of obtaining self-bias, with one battery, without current feedback, in a common-emitter amplifier. Explain the voltage drops in the resistors.

A.   For diagram, see the accompanying figure. The base-to-emitter

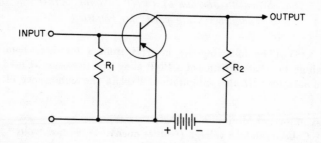

Fig. 3.186. Simplified schematic diagram of a PNP common-emitter amplifier using one battery and self bias.

bias (negative) is obtained by a voltage-divider scheme. Starting at the negative side of the battery, the voltage divider consists of the series combination of R2 and the high emitter-to-base resistance, dividing in series with the parallel combination of R1 and the low base-to-emitter resistance. This provides the required low value of negative voltage at the base (with reference to the emitter).

Q. 3.187. Draw a circuit diagram of a common-emitter amplifier with emitter bias. Explain its operation.

A. For the diagram, see the accompanying figure. The input signal is applied across resistor R2 to the base-emitter circuit. Bias for the base-

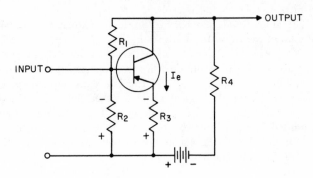

Fig. 3.187. Schematic diagram of a PNP common-emitter amplifier using emitter bias.

emitter circuit is the difference of two bias voltages. One is the voltage divider scheme described in Q. 3.186 above and the other is the drop across R3 (similar to a cathode resistor for a vacuum tube). R3 is introduced into the circuit for the purpose of bias stabilization. Reliable operation of a transistor over a wide range of temperatures, requires that the bias voltage and current remain stable. Variations of emitter-to-base junction resistance with temperature tend to cause bias changes unless external compensating circuits are used (such as R3).

D. The emitter-base junction resistance has a negative temperature coefficient of resistance, which causes a bias variation with temperature changes. One method of reducing the effect of this type of bias variation is to place a large value of resistor in series with the emitter lead. This resistor is called a *swamping* resistor. It causes the variation of the emitter-base junction resistance to be a small percentage of the total resistance in the emitter circuit. This technique stabilizes the bias and provides collector current stability over a wide range of temperatures (for example, $-65°C$ to $+125°C$). For best results in this technique, the base-circuit resistance should be as near zero as possible. One method of accomplishing this is to use a low-resistance transformer input to the base.

Q. 3.188. Explain the usual relationship between collector-to-base voltage and the alpha-cutoff frequency of a common emitter transistor amplifier.

A.   The alpha-cutoff frequency is only indirectly related to the collector-to-base voltage. This frequency is a function of the physical thickness of the base and increases as the base becomes thinner. As the base becomes thinner, the allowable base-to-collector voltage decreases. Thus it may be said that the alpha-cutoff frequency ordinarily increases as the permissable collector-to-base voltage decreases.

D.   The alpha-cutoff frequency is the high frequency at which the current gain of the transistor decreases by 3 db compared to its mid-frequency (flat) gain. The alpha-cutoff frequency is inversely proportional to the square of the base width and directly proportional to the minority carrier mobility. On this basis, NPN transistors are superior to PNP–types, because electrons have greater mobility than holes. To achieve the lowest base transit time, the base should be as thin as possible. However, this is limited by the permissable base-to-collector voltage. In transistor design, a trade off must be made between permissable base-to-collector voltage and the alpha-cutoff frequency.

Q. 3.189.   Why is stabilization of a transistor amplifier usually necessary? How would a *thermistor* be used in this respect?

A.   (a) Stabilization is usually necessary because transistor parameters, such as, reverse-bias collector current and emitter-base junction resistance, (see also Q. 3.187 above) vary with temperature. These cause changes in the transistor operating characteristics with respect to temperature. Specifically, emitter current increases with an increase of temperature.

(b) Emitter-current stabilization can be achieved with the aid of a thermistor (thermal-resistor) connected in an external circuit. A thermistor used for this purpose has a negative-temperature characteristic. That is, its resistance decreases with increases of temperature. The thermistor may be used as one element of a voltage divider. A resistor is placed in series with the emitter lead (see R3 in Fig. 3.187 above). Ordinarily (without stabilization), the collector current would tend to increase with an increase of temperature. This increase can be counteracted by increasing the reverse bias applied to the emitter through the voltage divider consisting of the thermistor and the emitter resistor. An increased temperature causes a decrease in resistance of the thermistor. This in turn raises the negative reverse bias applied to the emitter and decreases the net emitter forward bias. Consequently, the tendency of the collector current to increase is counteracted.

Q. 3.190.   Draw simple schematic diagrams of the following transistor circuits and explain their principles of operation. Use only one voltage source; state typical component values for low power—10 Mc operation:
  (a) Colpitts-type oscillator
  (b) Class-B push-pull amplifier

(c) **Common emitter amplifier**
(d) **A PNP transistor directly coupled to an NPN type.**

A. (a) For schematic of the Colpitts oscillator see the accompanying figure. For basic discussions and vacuum tube schematics, see Q. 3.74 and 3.367. In the transistorized oscillator shown in the figure, positive feedback is provided by placing the resonant tank circuit (L–C) in

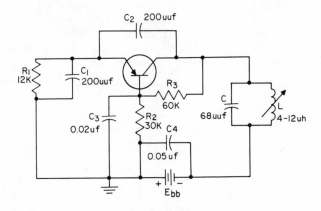

Fig. 3.190(a). Schematic diagram of a Colpitts oscillator for 10-mc operation.

parallel with the collector-to-base circuit. The circuit now becomes voltage, rather than current controlled. The feedback is taken from the junction of the two series capacitors C1 and C2 which are effectively across the tank. R2 and C3 provides emitter bias and a degree of oscillator-amplitude stability.

(b) The principle of a Class-B push-pull transistor amplifier is basically the same as for this type of amplifier using vacuum tubes (see Q. 3.107, 3.122, 3.374, 6.256 for basic principles). For a schematic of the transistor push-pull, Class-B amplifier see the accompanying figure. Resistors R1 and R2 are proportioned so that both transistors are operated at the collector-current-cutoff point. Both transistors will amplify only the positive portions of the applied base voltages. In this case, Q1 amplifies the first half (1) of the sine wave and remains at cutoff for the second half. Q2 amplifies the second half (4) of the sine wave. The center-tapped output transformer combines the two halves to form a sine-wave output in the secondary winding. Resonating the two transformers increases circuit efficiency and provides improved waveform (less distortion and harmonics) in the output.

(c) For the schematic of a common emitter amplifier, see the accom-

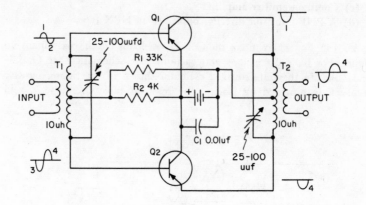

Fig 3.190(b). Schematic diagram of a Class-B push-pull amplifier for use at 10-mc.

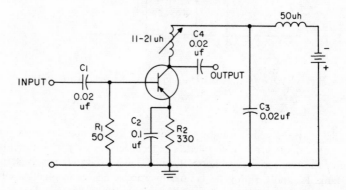

Fig. 3.190(c). Common-emitter amplifier with components for 10-mc operation.

panying figure. For principles of operation, see Q. 3.186 and 3.187 above.

(d) For a schematic of a PNP-transistor directly coupled to an NPN–type, see the accompanying figure. This scheme operates by virtue of the fact that the polarity of an input signal necessary to increase the conduction of the PNP–transistor is opposite to that required to increase the conduction of the NPN transistor. Since a signal polarity reversal occurs in Q1 from base to collector, this condition is satisfied. The proper bias for Q1 is established by the action of the voltage divider consisting of R1 and R2. The bias for Q2 is established by the collector current of Q1 flowing through the emitter to base circuit of Q2. The polarity of the base of Q2 is positive with respect to its emitter, thus providing forward

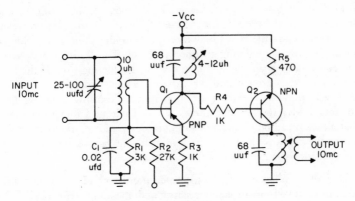

Fig. 3.190(d). A PNP transistor directly coupled to an NPN-type for 10-mc operation.

base-to-emitter bias. Note that the collector of Q2 is grounded for d–c and the collector-to-base potential is actually applied in reverse polarity to the emitter of Q2. This is similar to a vacuum tube amplifier wherein the plate voltage is actually applied as a negative potential to the cathode.

Q. 3.191. Discuss etched-wiring printed circuits with respect to the following:
  (a) Determination of wiring breaks.
  (b) Excessive heating.
  (c) Removal and installation of components.

A. (a) Wiring breaks are determined by point-to-point continuity checking with an ohmmeter. (If voltage exists in the circuit involved, voltage tracing could be used with the aid of an ohmmeter. Signal tracing with an oscilloscope is sometimes desirable.) Since there may be many common points permanently connected to the wire in question, a physical layout of the printed circuit board would be desirable to assist in locating the break. In many cases, the break can be repaired by soldering or by connecting an external wire across it.

(b) Etched wiring printed circuit boards are constructed of various materials such as epoxy and mylar. The etched wiring is attached to the board with a cement or other bonding agent. Such boards are subject to damage caused by excessive heat. Such heat can cause distortion of the board, or stresses which may result in cracks, wire breaks, or lifting of the etched wire from the boards.

(c) The components may be mounted on the boards by placing the component leads directly on a printed circuit finger and welding or soldering to the finger. Alternatively, the lead may be placed through a printed-circuit hole or eyelet. Generally, components are mounted only on one side of the board with their leads inserted into holes or eyelets. The other side of the board may then be dip soldered, or wave soldered, accomplishing all soldering in one operation. The leads of a defective component are usually removed with a small soldering iron. If the leads are welded, they are cut and the surface is cleaned in preparation for a new weld or for a solder repair. In removing transistors having three (or four leads) special attachments are available to a soldering iron so that all leads can be unsoldered simultaneously and the transistor pulled out of the board. Otherwise, one lead at a time can be unsoldered and the transistor gradually *rocked* out of the board.

Q. 3.192.   What is a junction tetrode transistor? How do they differ from other transistors in base resistance and operating frequency?

A.   (a) A tetrode transistor is one which is constructed in the same manner as a three-terminal PNP or NPN transistor except for the addition of an extra terminal to the base region.

(b) The base resistance is substantially lower than in a three-terminal transistor and the operating frequency is increased considerably.

D.   Because of the fourth terminal and its associated bias (negative for an NPN), a voltage gradient occurs across the base. Because of this gradient, forward bias (emitter-negative with respect to base) occurs only over a small portion of the emitter-base junction. In addition, current flow between base and collector also occurs over a small area of the base-collector junction. Because of the small areas involved, the effective input and output transistor capacitances are substantially reduced and the high-frequency response is substantially increased.

ANTENNAS

Q. 3.193.   Explain the voltage and current relationships in one-wavelength antenna; half-wavelength (dipole) antenna; quarter-wavelength "grounded" antenna.

A.   (a) In a one-wavelength antenna, the current is minimum at both ends and at the center of the antenna. Simultaneously, the voltage is maximum at these points. This may be seen clearly in the accompanying figure.

(b) For a half-wavelength antenna, see Figure 6.515.

(c) For a quarter-wavelength "grounded" antenna, the ground acts as a *mirror* to supply the second half of a half-wave antenna. The maximum current is therefore at the ground point, as is the minimum voltage. At the top of the antenna, the current is minimum and the voltage maximum.

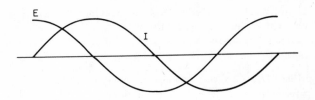

Fig. 3.193(a). Voltage and current distribution along a one-wavelength antenna (full-wave antenna).

D.   See Q. 6.514; see also Q. 3.5, 3.6 and 3.7 in Sup. No. 1. In addition refer to "Antennas" in the main book index for numerous references.

Q. 3.194.   What effect does the magnitude of the voltage and current, at a point on a half-wavelength antenna in "free space" (a dipole), have on the impedance at that point?

A.   The impedance measured at any point on a dipole in free space, is equal to the ratio of the voltage to the current at that point. (The actual magnitude of the values of voltage and current is of no consequence, other than to establish the ratio, $Z = \dfrac{E}{I}$.)

Q. 3.195.   How is the operating power of an AM transmitter determined using antenna resistance and antenna current?

A.   The operating (output) power is found by multiplying the square of the antenna current by the antenna resistance.

D.   See Q. 4.66, 4.67, 4.68, 4.70, 6.531, 3.321.

Q. 3.196.   What kinds of fields emanate from a transmitting antenna and what relationships do they have to each other?

A.   See Discussion for Q. 3.14, above.

Q. 3.197.   Can either of the two fields that emanate from an antenna produce an emf in a receiving antenna? If so, how?

A.   This question is highly theoretical and of doubtful value since it appears that the two fields are always present in a radiated wave (see Q. 3.196 above), and are interdependent. However, if it is assumed for example, that only the electromagnetic wave intercepts a receiving antenna (correctly polarized) a voltage will be induced in the receiving antenna. However, this immediately sets up an electrostatic field in the receiving antenna, causing current to flow and thus produce its own electromagnetic field. This locally restores the condition of the two interdependent fields. Similarly, it might be considered that the electrostatic field only intercepts a correctly polarized receiving antenna. A potential difference will be induced across the antenna, causing current to flow in the antenna. As above, the twin and interdependent fields will again be produced.

Q. 3.198. Draw a sketch and discuss the horizontal and vertical radiation patterns of a quarter-wave vertical antenna. Would this also apply to a similar type of receiving antenna?

A.   (a) The patterns are given in the accompanying figures. Note that the horizontal radiation pattern is omnidirectional and radiation is

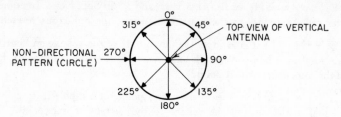

Fig. 3.198(a). Horizontal radiation pattern of a quarter-wave vertical antenna.

equal for all azimuth angles. In part *b* of the figure (vertical pattern), observe that the strength of radiation is greatest along the horizon and is reduced practically to zero at an angle of 90 degrees above the horizon. (See also Q. 3.224 and 3.252.)

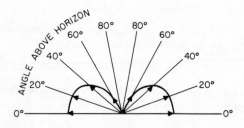

Fig. 3.198(b). Vertical radiation pattern of a quarter-wave vertical antenna.

(b) The same basic patterns apply to transmitting and receiving antennas.

Q. 3.199. Describe the directional characteristics, if any, of horizontal and vertical loop antennas.

A. (a) For horizontal loop antenna, see Q. 3.252(d).

(b) For vertical loop antenna, see Q. 3.252(c) and Q. 6.648.

Q. 3.200. In speaking of radio transmissions, what bearing does the angle of radiation, density of the ionosphere and frequency of emission have on the length of the skip zone?

A. (a) Angle of radiation: The smaller the angle of radiation at which a wave leaves the earth, the greater will be the length of the skip zone.

(b) Density of the ionosphere: The greater the density of the ionosphere, the more wave refraction (bending) takes place and the shorter will be the length of the skip zone.

(c) Frequency of emission: In general, the higher the frequency (below a critical value) the longer will be the skip zone.

D. The subject of "skip zone" is of necessity covered very inadequately by this question. Many variables and special conditions affect the phenomena of "skip." For more detailed information, it is recommended that the reader consult a book specializing in radio transmission. An excellent discussion may also be found in the ARRL Handbook, or other amateur radio handbooks. (See also Q. 3.245 and Q. 3.242 through 3.244.)

Q. 3.201. Why is it possible for a sky-wave to "meet" a ground wave 180 degrees out of phase?

A. Since the paths traveled by the sky wave and ground wave are of different lengths, the combined waves at a receiving antenna are usually out of phase. If the sky wave arrives at the receiving antenna such that its path is exactly one-half wavelength longer (or an odd multiple thereof) than the path of the ground wave, the two waves will be 180 degrees out of phase and severe fading will occur.

D. See Q. 3.503.

Q. 3.202. What is the relationship between operating frequency and ground-wave coverage?

A. In general, ground-wave coverage decreases with increasing frequencies. For frequencies above 5 to 10 megacycles, the reliable ground-wave coverage may be only a few miles.

D. See Q. 3.243, 3.242, 3.244, 3.245.

Q. 3.203. Explain the following terms with respect to antennas (transmission or reception):
(a) Field strength
(b) Power gain

(c) **Physical length**
(d) **Electrical length**
(e) **Polarization**
(f) **Diversity reception**
(g) **Corona discharge**

A. (a) Field strength (or field intensity): The signal voltage induced in an antenna, measured in millivolts or microvolts per meter. (See Q. 4.203, 4.61.)

(b) Power gain: The power gain of a given transmitting antenna is the ratio of the power radiated (in its maximum direction of radiation), compared to the power radiated by a standard (usually dipole) antenna. Both antennas must have the same polarization. (See Q. 4.273 for antenna field gain.)

(c) Physical length: See Q. 3.221, 3.223, 3.218.

(d) Electrical length: See Q. 3.221 and 3.218.

(e) Polarization: The polarization of an antenna is determined by its position with respect to the earth. (The polarization is determined by the direction of the electric field which is parallel to the physical plane of the antenna.) Thus, a vertical antenna is vertically polarized and a horizontal antenna is horizontally polarized.

(f) Diversity reception: See Q. 3.503.

(g) Corona discharge: See Q. 7.107 through Q. 7.110, Q. 7.113 and Q. 7.114.

Q. 3.204. What would constitute the ground plane if a quarter-wave grounded(whip) antenna, 1 meter in length, were mounted on the metal roof of an automobile; mounted near the rear bumper of an automobile?

A. (a) If this antenna were mounted on the metal roof, the roof would act as the ground plane since the length of the roof is an appreciable part of a wavelength (4 meters).

(b) If the antenna were mounted on or near the rear bumper, the bumper would act partially as the ground plane. Capacitive coupling to the earth would enable the earth to also act as part of the ground plane. The effectiveness of the bumper alone would depend largely upon its being an appreciable portion of a wavelength, at the frequency involved.

Q. 3.205. Explain why a "loading coil" is sometimes associated with an antenna. Would absence of the coil mean a capacitive antenna impedance?

A. (a) A "loading coil" is required to operate an antenna at a lower frequency than its actual length would normally permit. See Q. 3.218 and 3.222.

(b) Absence of a "loading coil" would mean that the antenna input would *look* like a capacitive reactance and depending on the magnitude of the reactance it might not be possible to feed power into the antenna. (See also Q. 3.218.)

Q. 3.206. **What radio frequencies are useful for long distance communications requiring continuous operation?**

A.   See Q. 3.243.

Q. 3.207. **What type of modulation is largely contained in "static" and "lightning" radio waves?**

A.   See Q. 3.246.

Q. 3.208. **Will the velocity of signal propagation differ in different materials? What effect, if any, would this have on wavelength or frequency?**

A.   (a) For velocity of propagation, see Q. 3.220.

(b) Assuming the wave has been generated externally to the material through which it is being transmitted; the type of material has no effect on its frequency. However, considering a constant frequency and materials exhibiting a lesser propagation velocity than free space, the measured wavelength along the material will be shorter than in free space.

Q. 3.209. **Discuss series and shunt feeding of quarter-wave antennas with respect to impedance matching.**

A.   Although not specifically stated, the question refers to vertical, quarter-wave antennas; ungrounded for series feed and grounded for shunt feed.

(a) In the series fed case, the bottom of the quarter-wave antenna must be insulated from ground. The impedance at the base (to ground) of the antenna is about 38 ohms. If maximum efficiency is not required, the antenna can be fed directly with a 50-ohm coaxial cable. The outer conductor is grounded (to the ground radials) and the center conductor connects to the insulated base of the antenna. For greater efficiency and lines of greater impedances, a tunable series LC network is connected between the base of the antenna and ground. The input power is inductively coupled to the series coil, which is resonated with the series capacitor to the operating frequency. This provides an excellent impedance match to the antenna, since maximum series antenna current will then be present.

(b) By the use of a shunt-feed system, it is possible to ground the base of the antenna, resulting in a savings of construction costs. In this system, the transmission line is terminated at a specified distance from the base of the antenna. A wire from the center conductor of the coaxial-transmission line is then stretched upward at an angle of approximately

45 degrees to a predetermined point on the antenna. The outer conductor of the line is grounded at its end to the ground radial system. A voltage is induced into the antenna by a magnetic field set up by a loop, consisting of the slant-wire, the lower portion of the antenna and the ground return from the base of the antenna, to the outer conductor of the coaxial line. A correct impedance match is obtained by varying the height at which the slant wire is connected to the antenna. For the common 70-ohm coaxial line, this connecting point will be approximately one-fifth of the total tower height.

Q. 3.210. Discuss the directivity and physical characteristics of the following types of antennas:
  (a) **Single loop**
  (b) **V-beam**
  (c) **Corner-reflector**
  (d) **Parasitic array**
  (e) **Stacked array**

A.   (a) Single loop: For photo and discussion of physical characteristics see page 648 (Appendix IV). Directivity characteristics are also discussed in Appendix IV; however, for shorter discussion and figures, see Q. 3.252(c), Q. 6.648 and 6.656.

(b) V–beam: The "V" antenna consists of two heavy wires in the form of a horizontal "V." (This is one form of a so-called, "longwire" antenna.) When each leg of the "V" is made one-wavelength long, the angle between the wires should be about 75 degrees. The directivity of the "V" antenna is along a line bisecting the "V" (bi-directional). However, the ends of the wires can be terminated resistively and the antenna becomes unidirectional in the direction of the open "V." Terminated "V" antennas have a wide bandwidth and gains in the order of 10 to 15db. The angle of radiation is largely in the horizontal direction and the pattern may be quite sharp (highly directive) if wires several wavelengths long are employed.

(c) Corner reflector: The corner-reflector antenna consists of the reflector and a half-wave dipole antenna. The reflector is made of two flat conducting sheets which are joined (for highest gain) at an angle of about 45 degrees. The reflector is mounted like an open book held vertically. The dipole is mounted vertically, a half wavelength from the joined sheets, along a line bisecting the 45 degree angle, inside of the "V" formed by the two sheets. This antenna has greater gain than the parabolic reflector type and is easier to construct. Maximum directivity is along the bisector of the corner angle and is mainly confined to the horizontal plane. This antenna is unidirectional.

(d) Parasitic array: The simplest parasitic array consists of a half-wave horizontal driven dipole and a reflector. The reflector is a rod (or tubing) about five percent longer than the dipole and mounted about one-quarter wavelength behind it on the same horizontal plane. However, the reflector has no direct electrical connection to the antenna and receives its energy entirely by induction. The practical length of the reflector may be determined by the formula

$$L = \frac{492}{f(mc)} \text{ feet}$$

The length of a dipole may be determined by the formula

$$L = \frac{462}{f(mc)} \text{ feet}$$

Addition of a reflector has the following effects on the normally bi-directional directivity of a simple dipole:

1. The array becomes basically unidirectional (in the direction opposite to the reflector).
2. The gain of the antenna is increased.
3. The unidirectional pattern is sharper than for the simple dipole.
4. The bandpass is reduced.
5. The dipole input impedance is reduced. The radiation of either the simple dipole or the parasitic array is mainly in the horizontal plane.

(e) Stacked array: A stacked array may be formed by mounting one driven dipole above another and is generally used with a reflector mounted behind each dipole. (Much more elaborate stackings are possible with numerous vertically stacked dipoles and reflectors. These are also frequently expanded in a broadside manner.) Stacking has the following effects compared to a single driven dipole:

1. Sharper directivity in the vertical plane.
2. Increase in gain of about 1.5 to 1.
3. Discrimination against rearward reception of about 3 to 1.
4. An increase in the dipole driving impedance.
5. Improved bandpass, compared to the single parasitic array. For a single-frequency band antenna, the vertical stacking of the elements will be about one-half wavelength. This is basically a unidirectional antenna.

Q. 3.211. Draw a sketch of a coaxial (whip) antenna; identify the positions and discuss the purposes of the following components:
    (a) Whip
    (b) Insulator
    (c) Skirt
    (d) Trap
    (e) Support mast
    (f) Coaxial line
    (g) Input connector

A. See the figure.

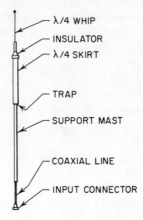

Fig. 3.211. Coaxial (whip) antenna showing all component parts.

(a) Whip: The top half (quarter-wavelength) of the radiating elements. (The other half of the radiating elements is the skirt, described below.) The whip is an electrical extension of the inner conductor of the coaxial-transmission line.

(b) Insulator: Required to insulate the center-conductor whip from the conducting skirt.

(c) Skirt: A metal cylinder mounted just below the insulator, and which is a quarter-wavelength long. This element, plus the whip completes the half-wave dipole radiator.

(d) Trap: A portion of the skirt forming a shorted quarter-wave transmission line section (for discussion, see Q. 4.202). The open end of the quarter-wave section represents a very high impedance at the operating frequency. This effectively insulates the bottom of the skirt from the outer conductor of the coaxial line (going through its center) permitting the skirt to act as a radiating element. The skirt receives its excitation energy at the center-feed point of the coaxial-line outer conductor, which is at the extreme top of the skirt.

(e) Support Mast: The mast supports the antenna structure. When a rigid coaxial line is employed, this item may be used as the support mast. However, for greater mechanical strength, the support mast may be a thick metal tubing or pipe, insulated from the skirt, surrounding either a rigid or flexible coax line. If a flexible coax line is used to feed the antenna, it may be supported at the skirt, using an insulated mounting support.

(f) Coaxial Line: A transmission line which guides the r–f energy from the transmitter to the coaxial-whip antenna. This is a shielded unbalanced transmission line (see discussion).

(g) Input Connector: A coaxial-type connector for connecting the coaxial line (from the transmitter) to the coaxial-whip antenna.

D.   A 72 ohm coaxial line is commonly used to feed the coaxial-whip antenna. The skirt is connected to the outer conductor of the coaxial line at its extreme upper portion, while the inner conductor continues for an additional one-quarter wavelength (electrical). Thus, effectively, the co-axial transmission line is "terminated" at the junction of the skirt and the quarter-wave, center-conductor radiator. The line feeds an actual half-wave antenna at its center point (72 ohms) and thus the impedance of the line is matched and there are practically no standing waves on the line. This helps to keep the radiation angles low, raising the efficiency of the antenna.

Q. 3.212.   Why are insulators sometimes placed in antenna guy wires?

A.   See Q. 3.504.

TRANSMISSION LINES

Q. 3.213.   What is meant by the *characteristic* (surge) impedance of a transmission line; to what physical characteristics is it proportional?

A.   (a) The characteristic (surge) impedance of a transmission line is the input impedance of a theoretically infinitely long line. In addition, if an impedance equal to this value is used to terminate a line of any given finite length, the same value of impedance appears at the input terminals of the line. The characteristic impedance also, is equal to the ratio of the voltage to the current along an infinite line, or a line terminated in its own characteristic impedance. This type of termination makes any line look like an infinitely long line. (See also Q. 4.77.)

(b) For the effect of physical properties on characteristic impedance, see Q. 6.502, 4.198, 4.199 and 4.202.

Q. 3.214.   Why is the impedance of a transmission line an important factor with respect to matching "out of a transmitter" into an antenna?

A.   For maximum power transfer from the transmitter to the transmission line, the input impedance of the transmission line must match the output impedance of the transmitter. Also, for maximum power transfer from the transmission line to the antenna, the transmission line impedance must match the input antenna impedance. This principle is no different than impedance matching for maximum power transfer in other types of circuits (i.e., audio power output circuits). (See also Q. 4.22.)

Q. 3.215.   What is meant by "standing waves"; "standing-wave ratio (SWR)," and "characteristic impedance" as referred to transmission lines? How can standing waves be minimized?

A.   (a) "Standing" waves are apparent stationary waves of voltage or current appearing on a transmission line (or antenna). They are stationary from the point of view that their maxima and minima always occur at the same physical points along the line (or antenna). Standing waves are created when a line is not terminated in its characteristic impedance. In this event, the incident waves from the generator are reflected to some degree at the end of the line. The reflected waves combine continuously with the incident waves causing *standing waves* to be formed along the line.

(b) "Standing-wave ratio" (SWR) is the ratio of maximum current (or voltage) along a line to the minimum current (or voltage) along the line. The ratio is commonly expressed as a number larger than one.

(c) For characteristic impedance, see Q. 3.213 above.

(d) Standing waves along a line can be minimized by terminating the line in an impedance equal to the characteristic impedance of the line. If this impedance is a pure resistance, there will be no standing waves and the line will be *flat,* or will appear to be infinitely long.

Q. 3.216.   If standing waves are desirable on a transmitting antenna, why are they undesirable on a transmission line?

A.   Standing waves are generally undesirable on a transmission line because of the following:

(a) Their presence indicates a mismatch at the antenna and thus, a loss of power being fed to the antenna.

(b) In the case of open-type lines, radiation will occur from the line, modifying the antenna pattern.

(c) A high standing-wave ratio on a transmission line may cause overheating, or arcing on the line, or in its associated circuits and traps.

(d) The higher the standing-wave ratio, the greater will be the losses on the transmission line.

D.   A simple straightforward answer to this question is not possible. It is true that for many antenna designs, a high standing-wave ratio is necessary and desirable. These are antennas of the "resonant" type such as quarter-wave, half-wave, or similar antennas. On the other hand there is a class of "long-wire" antennas which may be resistively terminated to have no standing waves. Examples of these are the straight-long wire, the "V" antenna and the rhombic antenna.

On the other hand, where space is at a premium (for example, on shipboard), particularly at low frequencies, the "lead-in" to the antenna may be made a resonant portion of the antenna proper. Then again, some high frequency transmission lines are deliberately operated as "tuned" or "resonant" lines and normally require the presence of standing waves for proper operation and impedance matching. In addition, some antennas are operated on several widely varying frequencies, (frequently harmonically related) causing the antenna input impedance to vary greatly. In such cases, the line is usually "tuned" (resonant) to match the antenna input impedance and standing waves necessarily exist on the line.

Q. 3.217. What is meant by "stub-tuning"?

A. "Stub-tuning," (or "stub-matching) refers to the use of short (tuned) lengths of transmission line, which are connected to the main transmission line near the antenna. Such stubs are used to reduce or eliminate standing waves on the main transmission line.

D. If a long transmission line is used to feed an antenna, it is not always feasible to match the transmission line properly to the antenna. However, to reduce line losses, it is desirable to reduce standing waves by matching the load to the line. At some fraction of a wavelength (less than a quarter-wave length) from the antenna, the line appears as a reactance of a definite value. If a stub (shorter than one-quarter wavelength) is attached to the main line at the chosen point, it will have an equal and opposite reactance to that on the main line. Thus, the effective line reactance at the attachment point is cancelled, and the main line *sees* only a resistance equal to the characteristic-line impedance. Thus, the line is matched and minimum standing waves result.

Q. 3.218. What would be the considerations in choosing a solid-dielectric cable over a hollow pressurized cable for use as a transmission line?

A. The question appears to be worded in reverse since the performance of the pressurized cable is superior. However, considerations for choosing a solid-dielectric cable (coaxial) would include the following:
(a) Less expensive.
(b) Easier to install, since it is more flexible.
(c) Tolerance to the higher losses.
(d) Does not require special plumbing-type connections.

D. See Q. 4.200.

FREQUENCY MEASUREMENTS

Q. 3.219. Draw a simplified circuit diagram of a grid-dip meter; explain its operation and some possible applications.

A.   (a) For the circuit diagram, see the accompanying figure.

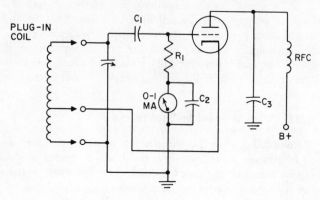

Fig. 3.219.   Simplified diagram of a grid-dip meter.

(b) The grid-dip meter is basically an oscillator (Hartley in this case) with a coil conveniently mounted so it can be easily coupled to the circuit under test. A set of plug-in coils are provided to cover a wide band of frequencies. Its operation is quite simple. When it is desired to measure the resonant frequency of a non-operating tank circuit, the probe coil is coupled loosely to the tank coil and the capacitor is varied until the meter dips to its lowest point. The frequency is then read directly from the grid-dip meter tuning dial. The meter dips because the tank circuit absorbs energy from the oscillator at the resonant frequency. This reduces the amplitude of oscillations and the oscillator grid current decreases causing a dip on the meter.

(c) Some possible applications are:

(1) To measure resonant frequency of a tuned circuit.

(2) To find undesired resonances in receiver or transmitter circuits.

(3) Use as a signal generator to align receivers.

(4) Can be used to measure r–f inductances and capacitances in conjunction with a standard capacitance or standard inductance.

Q. 3.220.   Draw a simplified circuit diagram of an absorption wavemeter (with galvanometer indicator); explain its operation and some possible applications.

A.   (a) For schematic see the accompanying figure. See also Q. 3.498.

(b) Some applications are:

(1) To measure the frequency of a self-excited oscillator.

(2) To find parasitic oscillations in transmitters.

(3) To determine the frequency of operation of r–f amplifiers and/or frequency multipliers.

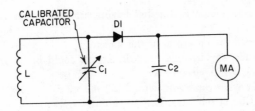

Fig. 3.220. Absorption-type wavemeter. D1 and C2 provide dc for the galvonometer.

D. See Q. 3.498 and Q. 6.638.

Q. 3.221. Draw a block diagram, showing only those stages which would illustrate the principle of operation of a secondary frequency standard. Explain the functions of each stage.

A. For block diagram, see the accompanying figure. The multivibrator (10 kc) is the basic oscillator and is accurately synchronized by the

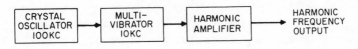

Fig. 3.221. Simplified block diagram of a secondary-frequency standard.

100 kc crystal oscillator. The harmonic amplifier may have switchable tuned circuits to amplify the higher harmonic frequencies which normally decrease rapidly in amplitude. Harmonics of both 100 kc and 10 kc are provided, with the 100 kc harmonics exceeding 30 megacycles in frequency.

D. For discussions of how to use and calibrate a secondary frequency standard, see Q. 3.33 Sup. and Q. 3.34 Sup. (Sup. No. 1).

Q. 3.222. Draw a block diagram of a heterodyne frequency meter, which would include the following stages:
Crystal Oscillator
Crystal Oscillator Harmonic Amplifier
Variable Frequency Oscillator
Mixer
Detector and AF Amplifier
AF Modulator
Show RF input and RF, AF, and calibration outputs. Assume a band-

switching arrangement and a dial having arbitrary units, employing a vernier scale.

(a) Describe the operation of the meter.

(b) Describe, step-by-step, how the crystal could be checked against WWV, using a suitable receiver.

(c) Under what conditions would the AF modulator be used?

(d) Describe, step-by-step, how the unknown frequency of a transmitter could be determined by use of headphones; by use of a suitable receiver.

(e) What is meant by calibration check-points; when should they be used?

(f) If in measuring a frequency, the tuning dial should show an indication between two dial-frequency relationships in the calibration book, how could the frequency value be determined?

(g) How could this meter be used as an RF generator?

(h) Under what conditions would it be necessary to re-calibrate the crystal oscillator?

A.   For the block diagram, see the accompanying figure.

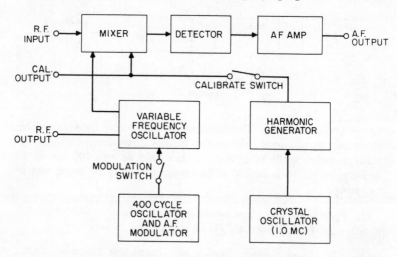

Fig. 3.222. Block diagram of a heterodyne-frequency meter.

(a) The unknown signal is fed to the *mixer* via the RF input where it is combined with a signal from the *variable frequency oscillator*. Due to the action in the mixer, the output not only contains the two original frequencies, but the sum and difference frequencies as well. This combination of frequencies, then, is fed to the *detector* whose output contains a signal equal to the difference of the two original frequencies—

the original frequencies and their sum being bypassed. If the two original signals are close enough in frequency, the difference frequency will be in the audio range and may be heard in the output of the *AF amplifier* by means of a suitable speaker or headphones. If the variable frequency oscillator is adjusted to make the difference frequency or beat become lower and lower in pitch until it disappears, the difference in frequencies is zero and the signal from the variable frequency oscillator has the same frequency as the unknown frequency. If the variable frequency oscillator has an accurately calibrated dial, the unknown frequency will now be known by reading the dial. The process of making the difference between the two frequencies zero is known as *zero beating*.

In order to be certain of the calibration of the variable frequency oscillator dial, facilities have been incorporated into the meter to provide signals of accurately known frequency to the mixer. In the meter shown in the block diagram, a 1.0 mc *crystal oscillator* with exceptionally good stability is used as a frequency standard. Means are provided to adjust the frequency of this oscillator to exactly 1.0 mc when required.

The output of the crystal oscillator is delivered to a *harmonic generator* for the purpose of obtaining harmonics of the 1.0 mc standard frequency that are of sufficient amplitude for use in the frequency range of the meter. If the meter is intended for use as high as 300 mc, the 300th harmonic must be strong enough to be heard in the *AF output* when beat with the variable frequency oscillator. By this method, the calibration of the variable frequency oscillator dial can be checked. If the calibration is faulty, means are provided for adjusting the dial, mechanically or electrically, so that the calibration is correct at the 1.0 mc harmonic check points.

It is often desirable to have the output of the variable frequency oscillator modulated with an audio frequency to assist in making accurate measurements. For this purpose, a *400 cycle oscillator and AF modulator* are provided. When such modulation is desired, the *modulation switch* is closed.

As shown on the diagram, an RF output terminal is shown. This output is useful for such purposes as receiver alignment, etc.

(b) If a suitable HF receiver is available, the meter can be calibrated against WWV by coupling the calibration output of the meter to the antenna input of the receiver and tuning the receiver to WWV on 5, 10, 15, 20, 25 or 30 mc. The frequency choice depends on the location of the receiving site, time of day, etc. With the receiver in the AM or phone mode, the calibrate switch of the meter is closed. If the crystal oscillator is *not* on frequency, a beat note will be heard which will be the difference between WWV and the 5th, 10th, 15th, 20th, 25th or 30th harmonic of the crystal oscillator. Which harmonic is heard will depend on which WWV frequency is being received.

By adjusting the trimmer provided on the crystal oscillator its frequency can be varied until zero beat is obtained with WWV. The crystal oscillator now is within approximately plus or minus 20 cycles of being correct *at that harmonic.* For better accuracy, it is well to adjust the crystal oscillator when the WWV signal is being modulated by its 440 cycle tone. Any frequency difference will be evidenced by an apparent waxing and waning of WWV's modulation, exact zero beat being obtained when the modulation remains steady in amplitude.

(c) Since the human ear cannot hear frequencies below approximately twenty cycles, the method of zero-beating the unknown signal against the output of the variable frequency oscillator produces results that are correct only to within approximately plus or minus twenty cycles. By modulating the variable frequency oscillator greater accuracy can be obtained. When the difference in the two frequencies is below audibility, the modulation of the variable frequency oscillator will grow stronger and weaker at a rate equal to the difference frequency. By observing this and adjusting the variable frequency oscillator so that the modulation is maintained at a constant amplitude, exact equality of the known and unknown signals can be obtained. The final accuracy of the measurement is limited only by the accuracy of a frequency standard and the calibration of the dial of the variable frequency oscillator.

(d) The process of using the meter and headphones to determine the frequency of a transmitter has already been described in the operation of the meter in the first paragraph of (a) above.

The unknown frequency of a transmitter, especially a distant one, can also be measured by using the meter in conjunction with a suitable receiver. This can be accomplished by first tuning in the transmitter on the receiver and then coupling the RF output of the meter to the antenna input of the receiver. Adjusting the variable frequency oscillator of the meter will produce a beat-note in the output of the receiver between the distant transmitter and the variable frequency oscillator. Zero beating the two signals will result in the variable frequency oscillator and the transmitter having the same frequency. The unknown frequency is read from the dial of the meter in the normal manner.

(e) Calibration check points are points or dial settings at which the 1.0 mc harmonics of the frequency standard should be heard at zero beat. They are used to assure that the frequency dial of the variable frequency oscillator is correctly adjusted to agree with the dial setting and frequency chart supplied with the meter.

For accurate and consistent results with the meter, these checkpoints should be used to check and adjust the calibration of the variable frequency oscillator *every* time a frequency is measured.

(f) The calibration information usually supplied with a meter of this type is in the form of a chart where specific dial settings are listed for discrete frequencies; the frequency spacing normally being uniform (100 cycles). It very often happens that the unknown frequency falls somewhere in between two listed adjacent frequencies and it is desired to know the unknown frequency more accurately than to the nearest 100 cycles. This may be determined by a process known as interpolation.

Let us suppose that the unknown frequency is zero beat at a dial setting of 173.6. Referring to the calibration chart, it is found that the dial setting for a frequency of 13248.3 kc is 173.1 and that for 13248.4 kc, the dial should read 174.2. It should be apparent that the unknown frequency is somewhere between 13248.3 and 13248.4 kc. On the assumption the dial setting vs frequency is a linear function over this small range, then the number of dial divisions per 100 cycles is 174.2—173.1 or 1.1. The number of dial divisions between 13248.3 kc and the unknown frequency is 173.6—173.1 or 0.5. The number of *cycles* between these two points, then, is $\frac{0.5}{1.1} \times 100$, or 45 cycles. This is added to the lower of the two listed frequencies so that the final frequency has been determined to be 13248.345 kc.

(g) The meter may be used as an RF generator for receiver alignment, etc., by using the RF output terminal coupled to the receiver under test. The variable frequency oscillator is an accurate frequency source but may be checked for accuracy by using the normal calibration check facilities as previously described.

Either a pure continuous wave or an amplitude-modulated wave can be obtained by proper positioning of the modulation switch.

(h) Normally the crystal oscillator's frequency should be checked on a routine basis; the period being determined by observation of the crystal's tendency to drift in frequency.

However, should the meter be used under unusual conditions such as high or low supply voltage or unusual climatic conditions, the crystal frequency should be checked against WWV and reset if found necessary.

Rough handling of the unit such as encountered in carrying it or shipping it dictates frequent crystal frequency checking. Any time the oscillator tube is replaced or any maintenance performed on the components of the oscillator circuit its frequency should be checked. It is good practice, also, to check the frequency when batteries are replaced in battery-powered use.

Q. 3.223. Draw a block diagram of an FM deviation (modulation) meter which includes the following stages:
Mixer
I–f amplifier
Limiter
Discriminator

Peak reading voltmeter

(a) Explain the operation of this instrument.

(b) Draw a circuit diagram and explain how the discriminator would be sensitive to frequency changes rather than amplitude changes.

A.   For the block diagram, see Fig. 3.223(a).

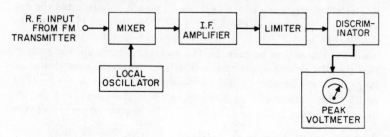

Fig. 3.223(a).   Block diagram of an FM deviation meter.

(a) Essentially, the FM deviation meter is a very simple FM receiver. Referring to the block diagram, a sample of the output of the FM transmitter and a signal from the local oscillator are combined in the mixer and the difference frequency is selected by a tuned circuit and passed to the I-F Amplifier. The I-F Amplifier provides the required amplification and selectivity for the signal and feeds the limiter. The function of the limiter is to provide an output of constant amplitude regardless of the amplitude of its input. The output of the limiter is a signal of fixed amplitude but varying in frequency according to the modulation of the original signal. The discriminator recovers the original A-F modulating signal from the modulated wave and delivers it to the peak reading voltmeter for measurement.

Since the frequency deviation is defined as the maximum instantaneous excursion of the signal frequency from the carrier frequency it corresponds to the peak amplitude of the modulating frequency. The peak amplitude of the A-F output from the discriminator is proportional to the frequency deviation. A suitable voltmeter, responding only to the *peak* amplitude of the discriminator A-F output, can be calibrated directly in terms of frequency deviation.

(b) Figure 3.223(b) illustrates a typical schematic of a discriminator, while the graph in Fig. 3.223(c) shows the response of such a discriminator to varying frequency.

The response, as shown, is the actual voltage obtained across resistors R_1 and R_2, in series. As can be seen, the instantaneous voltage output is dependent on the instantaneous frequency input. The conditions shown are for sine-wave modulation.

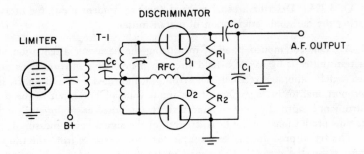

Fig. 3.223(b). Schematic diagram of an FM discriminator circuit.

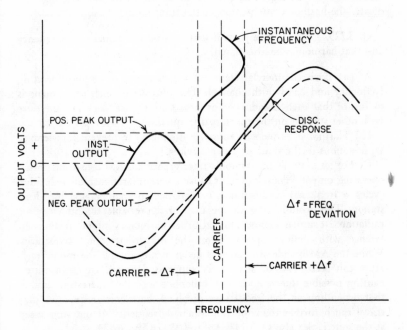

Fig. 3.223(c). The response of a discriminator to varying frequency.

The dashed response curve shown would be that obtained if the amplitude of the input was somewhat reduced. This would result in a reduced output for the same frequency deviation. This possibility is eliminated by the use of a limiter ahead of the discriminator, thus assuring constant amplitude input.

D. See Q. 4.217, 4.233, 4.238.

Q. 3.224. Describe a usual method (and equipment used) for measuring the harmonic attenuation of a transmitter.

A. One common method of measuring the harmonic attenuation of a transmitter is by use of a field strength meter. This instrument is an accurately calibrated receiver, whose output, indicated on a DB meter, is proportional to the logarithm of the input voltage. The input to the instrument is normally derived from a short wire, used as an antenna, and is thus proportional to the field strength of the signal being measured.

The actual procedure is very simple. At some distance from the transmitter site, the meter is first tuned to the fundamental frequency and the output DB noted. The meter is then tuned to the desired harmonic and the output DB again noted. The difference in the two readings, indicates the harmonic attenuation of the transmitter.

Q. 3.225. Why is it important that transmitters remain on frequency and that harmonics be attenuated?

A. (a) Each commercial transmitter is assigned a specific operating frequency and bandwidth channel. The purpose of such assignment is to insure that each broadcaster or broadcast service does not interfere with other stations on their assigned frequencies.

(b) Harmonic frequencies must be attenuated to prevent interference with stations in the same or other services.

D. For an example of harmonic interference, an AM broadcast station operating on 660 kilocycles might cause severe interference on 1320 kilocycles, a frequency which might be assigned to another AM broadcast station. This would occur in the case of appreciable second-harmonic radiation. In similar manner, higher order harmonics might create interference with stations operating on the higher-harmonic frequencies. While the AM broadcast band was given as an example, harmonic radiation can occur (if not adequately suppressed) from any transmitter, causing possible interference with other services. An interesting fact, is that depending on the frequencies involved, harmonic frequencies may travel much further than the fundamental frequency, if not suppressed at the source. See also Q. 3.232, 3.371, 3.373, 6.522, 6.523.

BATTERIES

Q. 3.226. How does a primary cell differ from a secondary cell?

A. See Q. 3.147.

Q. 3.227. What is the chemical composition of the electrolyte of a lead-acid storage cell?

A.   See Q. 3.150.

Q. 3.228.   Describe the care which should be given a group of storage cells to maintain them in good operating conditions?

A.   See Q. 3.205.

D.   See Q. 6.307, 6.317, 6.323.

Q. 3.229.   What may cause "sulphation" of a lead-acid storage cell?

A.   See Q. 3.207; 3.162.

Q. 3.230.   What will be the result of discharging a lead-acid storage cell at an excessively high current rate?

A.   See Q. 3.206.

Q. 3.231.   If the charging current through a storage battery is maintained at the normal rate, but its polarity is reversed, what will result?

A.   See Q. 3.161, 6.295.

Q. 3.232.   What is the approximate fully charged voltage of a lead-acid cell?

A.   See Q. 3.158.

Q. 3.233.   What steps may be taken to prevent corrosion of lead-acid storage cell terminals?

A.   See Q. 3.209.

Q. 3.234.   How is the capacity of a battery rated?

A.   In ampere-hours.

D.   See Q. 6.313.

MOTORS AND GENERATORS

Q. 3.235.   What is "power factor"? Give an example of how it is calculated. Discuss the construction and operation of dynamotors.

A.   (a) See Q. 3.34 for power factor.
(b) See Q. 3.505 for dynamotors. Also see Q. 6.385 for advantage and disadvantage.

Q. 3.236.   List the comparative advantages and disadvantages of motor-generator and transformer-rectifier power supplies.

A.   See Q. 3.396.

Q. 3.237.   What determines the speed of a synchronous motor? An induction motor? A d.c. series motor?

A.   See Q. 3.299.

Q. 3.238.   Describe the action and list the main characteristics of a shunt d.c. generator?

A.   See Q. 6.380.

Q. 3.239.   Name four causes of excessive sparking at the brushes of a d.c. motor or generator.

A.   See Q. 3.168.

Q. 3.240.   How may radio frequency interference, often caused by sparking at the brushes of a high-voltage generator, be minimized?

A.   See Q. 3.212.

Q. 3.241.   How may the output voltage of a separately excited a.c. generator, at constant output frequency, be varied?

A.   See Q. 3.166.

Q. 3.242.   What is the purpose of a commutator on a d.c. motor? On a d.c. generator?

A.   See Q. 3.169.

Q. 3.243.   What may cause a motor-generator bearing to overheat?

A.   See Q. 3.211.

Q. 3.244.   What materials should be used to clean the commutator of a motor or generator?

A.   See Q. 3.393.

Q. 3.245.   If the field of a shunt wound d.c. motor were opened while the machine is running under no load, what would be the probable result(s)?

A.   See Q. 3.167.

MICRO-WAVE EQUIPMENT

Q. 3.246.   Describe the physical structure of a klystron tube and explain how it operates as an oscillator.

A.   See Q. 8.48.

Q. 3.247.   Draw a diagram showing the construction and explain the principles of operation of a traveling-wave tube.

A.   See the figure. A traveling-wave amplifier is a micro-wave amplifier which may be used at frequencies well in excess of 7500 megacycles. The tube in the figure was designed for a mid-frequency of 3600 megacycles and a bandwidth of 800 megacycles. Bandwidths up to 5000 megacycles or more are possible using tubes with higher mid-frequency design.

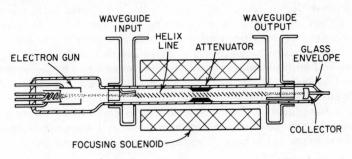

Fig. 3.247. The details of construction of a traveling-wave amplifier (Courtesy of International Telephone and Telegraph Corp.)

The tube is made up of the following major components:
1. Electron gun.
2. Helix line.
3. Focusing solenoid.
4. Collector anode.

The length of the helix may be 6 inches or more and consists of tightly wound wire. When in use, the tube is inserted into two waveguides as shown; one for input and one for output. Input and output coupling is accomplished by short stubs connected to each end of the helix and mounted so as to provide or receive energy from each waveguide (see the figure). The helix winding and collector are operated at a high positive potential (in this case, about 1600 volts) with respect to the cathode of the electron gun. The electron gun forms a beam of electrons which is focused electrically at the gun end and magnetically along the length of the helix by the focusing solenoid. The focused and accelerated beam is shot through the inside of the helix and parallel to its axis. It is picked up by the collector anode, located at the far end of the tube.

Energy in the form of electromagnetic waves are introduced to the tube via the input waveguide, travel along the helix wire and are coupled to the output waveguide. Because the waves follow the helix wire, their actual forward velocity is only about one-tenth that of light. At the acceleration voltage chosen, the beam of electrons inside the helix moves forward at a velocity slightly greater than that of the wave. (This is the condition of maximum tube gain.) The amplification of the tube occurs by virtue of the interaction of the electrostatic component of the electromagnetic field and the electron beam. The polarity of the electrostatic component will have the effect of producing velocity modulation of the electron beam (similar to klystron operation). When the electron beam is caused to speed up (positive electric field) it removes energy from the wave. When it is caused to slow down, it supplies energy to the wave (negative electric field). Now remember that the electron beam velocity is slightly greater than the wave velocity. A portion of the beam originating during a positive electric field will be further accelerated and will move relatively quickly out of the positive field and into the negative field farther down the tube. It will be slowed down by the negative field, giving up energy to it. Since it remains longer (slower) in the negative field, more energy is given up to the wave than was taken from it and amplification results. Amplification is governed by the relative velocity of the beam with respect to the wave and also (within limits) by the length of the helix. A longer helix produces greater gain.

Q. 3.248. Describe the physical structure of a multianode magnetron and explain how it operates.

A. The physical structure is illustrated in Figure 8.43. Principles of operation are given in Q. 8.70.

D. See Q. 8.45, 8.23.

Q. 3.249. Discuss the following with respect to waveguides:
(a) Relationship between frequency and size.
(b) Modes of operation.
(c) Coupling of energy into the wave guide.
(d) General principles of operation.

A. (a) For a rectangular waveguide, the height of the guide must be half wavelength or greater at the frequency in use.

(b) The mode of operation of a waveguide defines the manner in which the electric and magnetic fields arrange themselves inside of the waveguide. Each field configuration is called a "mode." Different modes may be excited by using different schemes of excitation. (Generally probes of some type.) The possible modes are determined by the shape of the waveguide. Modes are separated into two groups, as follows:

(1) The *transverse magnetic* (TM) group has its magnetic field in the direction transverse to the direction of propagation.

(2) The *transverse electric* (TE) group has its electric field transverse to the direction of propagation and has a component of magnetic field in this direction.

Each particular mode is identified by the letters for the group followed by two numerals. Examples are, $TM_{1,\,0}$ or $TE_{1,\,0}$.

(c) Coupling of energy to a waveguide may be accomplished in one of three principal ways, as follows:

(1) Insertion of a small loop of wire which couples to the electromagnetic field.

(2) Insertion of a small straight probe which couples to the electrostatic field.

(3) Linkage of the fields within the waveguide by external fields via the use of slots or holes in the wall of the waveguide.

(d) The waveguide operates on its ability to conduct electromagnetic waves within its boundaries. The energy is considered to be completely contained in these waves and is not carried as a current in wires. Because of skin effect, no energy escapes through the waveguide walls. Energy is introduced into and removed from a waveguide by one of the three methods described in (c) above.

Q. 3.250. Describe briefly the construction and purpose of a waveguide. What precautions should be taken in the installation and maintenance of a waveguide to insure proper operation?

A.   (a) For construction, see Q. 8.28.

(b) For purpose and characteristics, see Q. 8.30 and 3.502.

(c) For installation and maintenance, see Q. 8.27, 8.28, 8.29, 8.33, 8.34, 8.35.

Q. 3.251. Explain the principles of operation of a cavity resonator.

A.   A cavity resonator is a resonant circuit device, having very high Q and capable of being efficiently operated in the microwave frequency region. (See also Q. 3.502.) A cavity resonator is actually a measured section of waveguide whose resonant frequency depends upon its dimensions. Typical shapes for cavities are rectangular, cylindrical, spherical and doughnut. Cavities are energized in the same manner as waveguides, as described in Q. 3.249(c), above.

Q. 3.252. How are cavities installed in vertical waveguides to prevent moisture from collecting? Why are long horizontal waveguides not desired?

A.   (a) To prevent moisture accumulation, a half-wave stub with a drain hole may be installed perpendicular to the waveguide, just above the cavity. A pressurized guide will also prevent moisture accumulation.

(b) See Q. 8.29.

RULES AND REGULATIONS

Q. 3.253. Define the following words and phrases listed under Section 2.1 of the Commission's Rules. (R & R 2.1)

A. R & R 2.1: Definitions:

(a) Authorized frequency. The frequency assigned to a station by the FCC and specified in the instrument of authorization.

(b) Carrier: In a frequency stabilized system, the sinusoidal component of a modulated wave whose frequency is independent of the modulating wave; or the output of a transmitter when the modulating wave is made zero; or a wave generated at a point in the transmitting system and subsequently modulated by the signal; or a wave generated locally at the receiving terminal which, when combined with the sidebands in a suitable detector, produces the modulating wave.

(c) Base station: A land station in the land mobile service carrying on a service with land mobile stations.

(d) Coast station: A land station in the maritime mobile service.

(e) Earth station: A station in the earth-space service located either on the earth's surface or on an object which is limited to flight between points on the earth's surface.

(f) Fixed station. A station in the fixed service.

(g) Space station. A station in the earth-space service or the space service located on an object which is beyond, or intended to go beyond, the major portion of the earth's atmosphere and which is not intended for flight between points on the earth's surface.

(h) Harmful interference: Any emission, radiation or induction which endangers the functioning of a radio-navigation service or of other safety services or seriously degrades, obstructs, or repeatedly interrupts a radio-communication service operating in accordance with this chapter.

(i) Land Mobile Service. A mobile station in the land mobile service capable of surface movement within the geographical limits of a country or continent.

(j) Land station. A station in the mobile service not intended to be used while in motion.

(k) Mobile service. A service of radio communication between mobile and land stations, or between mobile stations.

(1) Primary standard of frequency. The primary standard of frequency for radio frequency measurements shall be the National Bureau of Standards, Department of Commerce, Washington, D.C. The operating frequency of all radio stations will be determined by comparison with this standard or the standard signals of station WWV of the National Bureau of Standards.

Q. 3.254. What is the frequency range associated with the following general frequency subdivisions? (R & R 2.101)
   (a) VLF
   (b) LF
   (c) MF
   (d) HF
   (e) VHF
   (f) UHF
   (g) SHF
   (h) EHF

A.   (a) VLF (very low frequency). Below 30 kc/s.
   (b) LF (low frequency). 30 to 300 kc/s.
   (c) MF (medium frequency). 300 to 3000 kc/s.
   (d) HF (high frequency). 3 to 30 Mc/s.
   (e) VHF (very high frequency). 30 to 300 Mc/s.
   (f) UHF (ultra high frequency). 300 to 3000 Mc/s.
   (g) SHF (super high frequency). 3 to 30 Gc/s.
   (h) EHF (extremely high frequency). 30 to 300 Gc/s.

Q. 3.255. What is meant by the following emission designations? (R & R 2.201)
   (a) A3
   (b) A3A
   (c) A5C
   (d) F3
   (e) F5
   (f) P3D

A.   (a) A3: Amplitude modulation, telephony, double sideband transmission.
   (b) A3A: Amplitude modulation, telephony, single sideband, reduced carrier.
   (c) A5C: Amplitude modulation, television, vestigial (partial) sideband.
   (d) F3: Frequency (or phase) modulation, telephony.
   (e) F5: Frequency (or phase) modulation, television.
   (f) P3D: Pulse modulation, telephony, amplitude modulated pulses.

Q. 3.256. What is the basic difference between type approval and type acceptance of transmitting equipment? (R & R 2.551)

A.   Type approval contemplates tests conducted by FCC personnel. Type acceptance is based on data concerning the equipment submitted by the manufacturer or the individual prospective licensee.

Q. 3.257. Define the following words and phrases listed under Section 89.3 of the Commission's Rules.

A. (a) Authorized bandwidth: The maximum width of the band of frequencies, as specified in the authorizations, to be occupied by an emission.

(b) Bandwidth occupied by an emission: The width of the frequency band (normally specified in kilocycles) containing those frequencies upon which a total of 99 percent of the radiated power appears, extended to include any discrete frequency upon which the power is at least 0.25 percent of the total radiated power.

(c) Station authorization: Any construction permit, license, or special temporary authorization issued by the Commission.

Q. 3.258. May stations in the Public Safety Radio Services be operated for short periods of time without a station authorization issued by the Commission? (R & R 89.51)

A. No radio transmitter shall be operated in the Public Safety Radio Services except under and in accordance with a proper station authorization granted by the Federal Communications Commission.

Q. 3.259. What notification must be forwarded to the Engineer in Charge of the Commission's district office prior to testing a new radio transmitter in the Public Safety Radio Service (which has been obtained under a construction permit issued by the Commission)? (R & R 89.53)

A. Procedure for obtaining a Radio Station Authorization and for Commencement of Operation:

(a) Persons desiring to install and operate radio transmitting equipment should first submit an application for a radio station authorization.

(b) When construction permit only has been issued for a base, fixed or mobile station and installation has been completed in accordance with the terms of the construction permit and the applicable rules of the Commission, the permittee shall proceed as follows:

(1) Notify the Engineer-in-Charge of the local radio district of the date on which the transmitter will first be tested in such manner as to produce radiation, giving name of the permittee, station location, call sign, and frequencies on which tests are to be conducted. This notification shall be made in writing at least two days in advance of the test date. FCC Form 456 may be used for this purpose. No reply from the radio district office is necessary before the tests are begun.

Q. 3.260. Where may standard forms applicable to the Public Safety Radio Services be obtained? (R & R 89.59)

A. To assure that necessary information is supplied in a consistent manner by all persons, standard forms are prescribed for use in connection with the majority of applications and reports submitted for Commission consideration. Standard numbered forms applicable to the Public Safety Radio Services may be obtained from the Washington, D.C. Office of the Commission, or from any of its engineering field offices.

Q. 3.261.   In general, what type of changes in authorized stations must be approved by the Commission? What type does not require Commission approval? (R & R 89.75)

A.   Authority for certain changes in authorized stations must be obtained from the Commission before these changes are made, while other changes do not require prior Commission approval. The following paragraphs describe the conditions under which prior Commission approval is or is not necessary.

(a) Proposed changes which will result in operation inconsistent with any of the terms of the current authorization require that an application for modification of construction permit and/or license be submitted to the Commission. The request for authorization shall be submitted on FCC Form 400, or, in the case of microwave stations, on FCC Form 402, and shall be accompanied by exhibits and supplementary statements as required by R & R 89.63.

(b) Proposed changes which will not depart from any of the terms of the outstanding authorization for the station involved may be made without prior Commission approval. Included in such changes is the substitution of various makes of transmitting equipment at any station provided the particular equipment to be installed is included in the Commission's "List of Equipment Acceptable for Licensing." In addition it must be designated for use in the Public Safety, Industrial, and Land Transportation Radio Services. The substitute equipment must employ the same type of emission and must not exceed the power limitations as set forth in the station authorization.

Q. 3.262.   The carrier frequency of a transmitter in the Public Safety Radio Service must be maintained within what percentage of the licensed value? Assume the station is operating at 160 Mc/s with a licensed power of 50 watts. (R & R 89.103)

A.   The carrier frequency must be maintained within .0005 percent.

Q. 3.263.   What is the authorized bandwidth and frequency deviation of Public Safety stations operating at about 30 Mc/s? At about 160 Mc/s? (R & R 89.107)

A.   (a) For 30 megacycles, the authorized bandwidth is 20 kilocycles and the frequency deviation is 5 kilocycles.

(b) For 160 megacycles the specifications are the same as (a) above.

Q. 3.264. What is the maximum percentage modulation allowed by the Commission's rules for stations in the Public Safety Radio Services which utilize amplitude modulation? (R & R 89.109)

A. The maximum is 100 percent on negative peaks.

Q. 3.265. Define "control point" as the term refers to transmitters in the Public Safety Radio Service. (R & R 89.113)

A. A control point is an operating position which:

(a) Must be under the control and supervision of the licensee.

(b) Is a position at which the monitoring facilities are installed.

(c) Is a position at which a person immediately responsible for the operation of the transmitter is stationed.

Q. 3.266. Outline the transmitter measurements required by the Commission's rules for stations in the Public Safety Radio Service. (R & R 89.115)

A. Transmitter measurements. (a) The licensee of each station shall employ a suitable procedure to determine that the carrier frequency of each transmitter, authorized to operate with a plate input power to the final radio-frequency stage in excess of 3 watts, is maintained within the tolerance prescribed. This determination shall be made, and the results thereof entered in the station records, in accordance with the following:

(1) When the transmitter is initially installed:

(2) When any change is made in the transmitter which may affect the carrier frequency or the stability thereof;

(3) At intervals not to exceed one year for transmitters employing crystal-controlled oscillators.

(4) At intervals not to exceed one month, for transmitters not employing crystal-controlled oscillators.

(b) The licensee of each station shall employ a suitable procedure to determine that plate power input to the final radio frequency stage of each base station or fixed station transmitter, authorized to operate with a plate-input power to the final radio frequency stage in excess of 3 watts, does not exceed the maximum figure specified on the current station authorization. Where the transmitter is so constructed making a direct measurement of plate current in the final radio frequency stage impracticable, the plate input to the final radio frequency stage is determined from a measurement of the cathode current. The required entry shall indicate clearly the quantities that were measured, the measured values thereof, and the method of determining the plate-power input from the measured values. This determination shall be made, and the results thereof entered in the station records, in accordance with the following:

(1) When the transmitter is initially installed;

(2) When any change is made in the transmitter which may increase the transmitter power input;

(3) At intervals not to exceed one year.

(c) The licensee of each station shall employ a suitable procedure to determine that the modulation of each transmitter, authorized to operate with a plate input power to the final radio-frequency stage in excess of 3 watts, does not exceed the limits specified. This determination shall be made and the results thereof entered in the station records, in accordance with the following:

(1) When the transmitter is initially installed;

(2) When any change is made in the transmitter which may affect the modulation characteristics;

(3) At intervals not to exceed one year.

(d) The determinations required by paragraphs (a), (b), and (c) of this section may, at the option of the licensee be made by any qualified engineering measurement service, in which case, the required record entries shall show the name and address of the engineering measurements service as well as the name of the person making the measurements.

(e) In the case of mobile transmitters, the determinations required by paragraphs (a) and (c) of this section may be made at a test or service bench: *Provided,* the measurements are made under local conditions equivalent to actual operating conditions; That after installation the transmitter is given a routine check to determine that it is capable of being satisfactorily received by an appropriate receiver.

Q. 3.267. What are the general requirements for transmitting the identification announcements for stations in the Public Safety Radio Service? (R & R 89.153)

A. Station identification.

(a) Except as provided in paragraph (b) of this section, the required identification for stations in these services shall be the assigned call signal.

(b) In lieu of meeting the requirements of paragraph (a) of this section, mobile units in the Police, Fire, Forestry-Conservation, Highway Maintenance, and Local Government Radio Services operating above 30 Mc/s may identify by means of an identifier other than the assigned call signal: *Provided,* that such identifier contain, as a minimum, the name of the governmental subdivision under which the unit is licensed; that the identifier is not composed of letters or letters and digits arranged in a manner which could be confused with an assigned radio station call signal: That the licensee notifies, in writing, the Engineer in Charge of the District in which the unit operates concerning the specific identifiers being used by the mobile units.

(c) Nothing in this section shall be construed as prohibiting the transmission of additional station or unit identifiers which may be necessary for systems operation: *Provided,* such additional identifiers are not to be composed of letters or letters and digits arranged in a manner which could be confused with an assigned radio station call signal.

(d) Except as indicated in paragraphs (e), (f), and (g) of this section, each station in these services shall transmit the required identification at the end of each transmission or exchange of transmissions, or once each 30 minutes of the operating period, as the licensee may prefer.

(e) A mobile station authorized to the licensee of the associated base station and which transmits only on the transmitting frequency of the associated base station is not required to transmit any identification.

(f) Except as indicated in paragraph (e) of this section, a mobile station shall transmit an identification at the end of each transmission or exchange of transmissions, or once each 30 minutes of the operating period, as the licensee may prefer. Where election is made to transmit the identification at 30 minute intervals, a single mobile unit in each general geographic area may be assigned the responsibility for such transmission, thereby eliminating any necessity for each unit of the mobile station to transmit the identification. For the purpose of this paragraph the term "each general geographic area" means an area not smaller than a single city or county and not larger than a single district of a state where the district is administratively established for the service in which the radio system operates.

(g) A station which is transmitting for telemetering purposes or for the actuation of devices, or which is retransmitting by self-actuating means a radio signal received from another radio station or stations, will be considered for exemption from the requirements of paragraph (d) of this section in specific instances, upon request.

Q. 3.268. When a radio operator makes transmitter measurements required by the Commission's rules for a station in the Public Safety Radio Service what information should be transcribed into the station's records? (R & R 89.175)

A.   The results and dates of the transmitter measurements and the name of the person or persons making the measurements.

Q. 3.269. What are the Commission's general requirements regarding the records which are required to be kept by stations in the Public Safety Radio Service? (R & R 89.177)

A.   Form of station records. (a) The records shall be kept in an orderly manner and in such detail that the data required are readily available. Key letters or abbreviations may be used if proper meaning or explanation is set forth in the record.

(b) Each entry in the records shall be signed by a person qualified to do so having actual knowledge of the facts to be recorded.

(c) No record or portion thereof shall be erased, obliterated, or willfully destroyed within the required retention period. Any necessary correction may be made only by the persons originating the entry who shall strike out the erroneous portion, initial the correction made and indicate the date of the correction.